Contents

contents

Q Trek

The Pursuit of Quality

A Guide to Achieving Quality
in Personal Community Care Services

Patrick S. Donlan

British Library Cataloguing in Publication Data
A catalogue record for this book is available from the
British Library.

ISBN 1 B74257 17 5

South East Institute of Public Health
Broomhill House
David Salomons Estate
Broomhill Road
Tunbridge Wells
Kent TN3 0XT

Tel: (01892) 515153
Fax: (01892) 516344

Acknowledgments

I hope this book is helpful to the many professionals who assisted me with my work through their ideas as part of the Institute's Quality Network Training. I wish to thank them for their robust participation in our discussions about what quality means in what has become known as the new NHS. The need for a book like this arose from those discussions, which happily continue today.

This book is a product of the *South East* Institute of Public Health, and I am especially grateful to Dr June Crown, SEIPH's Director, Dr Yvonne Doyle and Dr Christine Russell-Hodgson for their comments.

My wife Sarah has been totally enthusiastic and supportive in what was a new venture for me, and one which required much more time and energy than I had supposed. It has been a longer personal trek than I had imagined. Sarah read the text as it developed and provided excellent critical input. Also Angus Bentley and Brian Morrison were both detailed and perceptive in their comments about the text and I thank them for their contributions. Even my sons Ben and Chris had a hand in sorting out the language to make it more effective.

Lesley Hicken, my secretary, patiently found ways of translating the text from the obscure word processing programme in which it was originally constructed (and apparently known only to me) into one that other people used and understood. I appreciate both her skills and her patience.

Finally, I hope this book proves a useful aid to the many people involved in helping vulnerable people and that it assists them to move closer towards the elusive goal of quality in personal community care services.

Patrick S. Donlan
SEIPH
May 1996

Introduction

THIS book is about helping you make quality an everyday reality in what you do for other people. It is about demystifying "quality", particularly as the term is applied to the intensely personal services commissioned or provided by our health and social care systems. This book brings with it the hope of providing useful understandings of what people working in these care systems need to do every day to elevate the content and experience of their daily human contact beyond the merely administrative. It is the sensitivity of this human contact within the framework of the caring and healing processes that drives up quality of life for both service users and carers.

This book is about dangerous ideas that need to be hunted down, rounded up and brought in for questioning. All caring activity starts with our perceptions of problems, how to understand them and resolve them. These perceptions become crystallised into ideas, then philosophies – if they explain problems, or technologies – if they resolve them. Some of these ideas are so simple, so "obvious" that they are often overlooked. When they are accepted as obvious and as universally understood, they tend not to be discussed or questioned. That's when they become dangerous.

Complicating simple ideas seems to be the undeclared mission of most academics, whilst oversimplifying complex ideologies is the not-so-hidden agenda of many a management consultant. The obscure paths on which these specialists tread enchant newcomers more by the smoke than the light of the fires of human achievement. Ideas are analyzed and dissected almost to the point of extinction, and a perverse, joyless pride grows from knowing more and more about the complexities and the apparent impossibilities that exist and what can not work in the real world.

Esoteric approaches to the problem of quality often share the same fate: they do not travel well outside the world of ideas. The excitement they generate on campus and the enthusiasm they breed in the land of ideas often fail to translate in the world of physical and emotional need, of bed pans and bath seats and disadvantaged everyday living. The fact is that often the "ideas people" are too far away from the "care people" to either communicate with them or be influenced by them. The assumption is that those who are in the best position to improve quality in practice – the practitioners – are too inexperienced, too low in the organisational hierarchy, or too remote from theory to understand fully what they should be doing. This is the point at which theory (always necessary for developing understanding) has the effect of disempowering practitioners, lulling them into passive and unresponsive working lives. They become dulled, unaccustomed to demanding more of themselves but satisfied with doing just enough to get by.

The problem is that it is not very satisfying for the care professional to do only the minimum – just enough to get by. Most practitioners need to feel proud of what they do, and even though there may be little formal recognition of the value of their work with vulnerable people, their self esteem is injured when they know they are not giving of their best.

Mystification need not be part of the business of doing better what we already do well. However, what is useful is to unlock imaginative thinking in a way which gets the central "quality culture" message through to health and social care practitioners where they work every day. That message is this:

"No matter how well you do what you do for people, and no matter how satisfied your service users are with your performance, you can still find something which can be improved if you look for it!"

Improving the quality of what we do with and for others is an unending journey. On this journey, personal motivation and experience drive us toward practical achievements in a world where caring and helping are a daily expectation. This book is a practical guide for your journey into quality.

Throughout these pages you will find ideas that build on your own thinking, or paragraphs which say what you already know to be true but have not yet put into words. It is essential to get the words right, simply because the lack of clear statements about what you and your agency intend to achieve prohibits others involved in your work from understanding and sharing your concepts of quality and its management.

Here are some suggestions for developing your own critique for your quality initiatives:

* Do not assume that those with whom you work share your perception of what quality means

* Be sure you understand your own ideas (whether they are developed or not) before asking others to understand them

* Do not accept the ideas of others without testing them

* Recognize catchy one-liner insights as being too glib to be worthwhile unless they lead you to further understanding

* Recognize that ideas or one-liners accepted without criticism are substitutes for thinking and are therefore dangerous

* Do not use your newly understood good ideas to make others feel inadequate

* See how you can improve upon the ideas and suggestions in this book

* Use the margins to plot your own progress and in doing so learn how you learn!

Think of this as both a reference book and a work book. The broad margins are there for your notes and your ideas. Jot them in pencil, so that they can be erased or extended as your own ideas about quality develop.

This book should help you strip away the mystery surrounding quality. Get ready to reach out for the little intangibles that surround this concept. These intangibles are not easily understood in quantitative terms; they are the personal, qualitative components that make human contact worthwhile. They are the messages that come from caring contact which tell your service user that they are people of significance; they are people who make a difference!

Fundamentally you will be looking at the relationship between what you do and what you achieve. Quality services should be producing quality outcomes, but they are not the same thing. In the end, it is what you achieve that counts, not the feeling that you are doing well.

introduction

In no way will you find this book promoting the false idea that quality – as applied to personal health and social care services – is simple to achieve. In the end, there will still be many service users who will be in the very best position to tell you how the quality of their lives has been affected by what you have done. Look to them to help you understand how well you have brought quality into their lives.

The Demystification of Quality

THE NHS and Community Care Act 1990 has underscored the complexity of quality management by effectively legislating that quality cannot be truly encapsulated within the perspective of one single agency. Now, managing good enough health care necessarily includes negotiating for adequate and complementary social care. This means that quality health and social care services are linked together around a holistic or integrated assessment of the needs of a person, a community, and a population.

Quality services are those which you provide for people as the whole but complex human beings they are. The first great principle of quality in personal health and social care services reflects this:

PRINCIPLE 1
QUALITY IN PERSONAL HEALTH AND SOCIAL CARE IS UNIFYING AND INCLUSIVE RATHER THAN DISCRIMINATING AND EXCLUSIVE

So how are personal services different from services provided personally? Let's look to two national corporations and their experience of redressing some historically poor customer satisfaction levels.

British Rail services are designed to generate profits by meeting some of your transport needs. British Telecom and Mercury compete for a greater market share by providing a range of alternatives to meet your communication requirements. These are particular services you purchase to meet specific needs. It is of virtually insignificant interest to BR that you are unable to gain access to BT facilities, except inasmuch as they themselves might benefit as the alternative solution to your communication problem. Each corporation is service led, even though they may achieve a significant level of customer satisfaction within their specialist (exclusive) field. That is, each is only prepared to respond to the part of your needs that they individually recognise as their territory.

Personal health and social services are different. While they involve the energies of specialists and technically competent professionals, it is of the utmost importance that their activities are appropriate to the needs and requirements of the whole person. When these services fail to come together at the right time or in the right way, the most common complaint is that people feel they have been treated impersonally, like "just another client", another burden to the professionals. It is the personal nature of health and social care services that ultimately determines the quality of those services. They are person-centred and needs led!

The cultural shift to person-centred activity is not difficult in theory yet remains complex in practice. To be fully effective that shift must happen at both the personal and the organisational levels. It should be so subtle and comprehensive that it might prove difficult to distinguish the influence one level is having on the other. The shift need not baffle you, though it may be complex and have far reaching implications for the organisation.

When organisational change becomes over-complex and the upheaval is on a large scale, corporate "drama" erupts in the processes of change. The merely different becomes very difficult, and the difficult appears to be impossible.

Your achievement of quality in health and social care agencies will require change which is relatively free of dramatics. The right kind of change takes place with a view to something better happening in the future. The context for change is the agreed vision of what that "something better" should be. But the momentum of change is crucial to success. Every change needs its pace, the thoughtfully managed intervals of activity and consolidation which allow everyone to learn and adapt to that new learning. If your pace is set by the short term needs of the agency the change will not bring benefits for the longer term. But if your pace is set in the context of the longer term vision it is more likely to produce long term, well understood benefits. Achieving the right pace of change should ensure that the vision gains meaning and becomes reality even through the smallest transitional steps.

Quality achievement is really a matter of quality management. It means developing systems that are universally understood by the many agencies purchasing and providing care, reviewing the outcomes of the services provided, agreeing performance indicators and time targets, and establishing standards which both support the functions and measure their effectiveness. In this way the quality of what you do becomes evident by virtue of what you achieve.

the demystification of quality

Measuring quality in personal health and social services is not difficult, only different! Different, because the effectiveness of the professional or clinical input is interwoven with the interpersonal processes (the day-to-day dealings between people) which enable service users to benefit more fully. Different, because the quality of the outcome can only be measured within the context of the service user's life in the community.

The demystification of quality starts with challenging what is meant by the words we use every day in our work with others. "Quality" is one of today's growing number of "charter speak" words and phrases. It regularly takes its place in mission statements and glossy information brochures alongside other notables such as "empowerment" and "customer satisfaction." "Value for money" is still alive and well and hanging in there from the late 1980s but has been de-emphasized just a touch!

Unfortunately, the term "quality" is applied to health and social care, railway services, and the performance of BT engineers without much critical thinking that helps us understand what it actually means in any one of those settings. The term "quality" does not enjoy the common imagery of such excellent words as "table" or "geo-thermo-nuclear device."

What familiar picture does the word "quality" bring to mind? This is a good question and deserves more attention than it receives. Let's look at some offerings from the language of management consultancy. You can test the validity of each one by asking this simple question:

"How can I use this definition for improving what I do here and now?"

"Quality is (means)...

– getting it right first time."

– that which meets the customer's expectations."

– fitness for the purpose."

– degrees of excellence."

Whilst each of these statements may describe an aspect of quality, its process or products, each begs the question simply because it addresses no particular reality. Definitions of quality which do not address the issue of context are destined to remain empty. They remain cosmetic, masquerading as useable concepts from the world of ideas. They are superficial and facile because they fall foul of the second great quality principle, which is:

PRINCIPLE 2

QUALITY IS ALWAYS AND ONLY UNDERSTOOD WITHIN THE CONTEXT OF PURPOSE

For the moment, we will use a definition borrowed from industry and enshrined in British Standard # 5750: "Quality is the conformance to requirement." Like the others, it is somewhat unsatisfactory, and certainly not in any way personally satisfying. However, it is useful inasmuch as it more clearly identifies "context" as a crucial consideration.

Simply put, quality exists when the services you provide actually achieve their agreed effect. There has to be an objective, a requirement, a demand to be met before your functions, processes or outcomes could be measured as being of quality. And this is another way of stating the third great quality axiom:

PRINCIPLE 3

QUALITY IS PRIMARILY RELATED TO EFFECTIVENESS IN THE ACHIEVEMENT OF PURPOSE

This axiom forms the basis of all the following chapters. For now, we can deduce a corollary which is powerful enough to formulate the fourth great quality axiom:

PRINCIPLE 4

QUALITY ESSENTIALLY DEPENDS ON EFFICIENCY IN THE ACHIEVEMENT OF PURPOSE

Efficiency is a strong feature of quality services. The problem is, however, that no matter how efficient your services become through labour-saving technologies, they will have no quality whatsoever unless they achieve the purposes for which they were designed. They must primarily be effective. Preoccupation with efficiency can become an all consuming passion, a whirlwind of activity in itself, draining your energy which would be better spent tuning the responsiveness of services to human need.

Another difficulty is that quality is thought to be both objective and subjective. In one view, quality exists objectively when the purpose of an activity or service is achieved directly or indirectly by that activity or service. Subjectively, quality exists when people are satisfied that what was agreed and intended to be achieved has actually been achieved to or beyond their expectations.

Is quality an absolute? "Yes," because it is most helpful to think of quality in absolute terms. Quality services either exist or they do not. If the services are effective – that is, if they produce quality outcomes – they will show the consistency normally identified with quality services. There are strong arguments that quality exists when the purpose has been achieved to or beyond expectations, and that it doesn't when that purpose has not been achieved. This means you either have a quality service or you don't, depending on its effectiveness.

People tend to see quality as an absolute in everyday life. While there may be nothing which is always and undeniably of quality in itself, there can be a consensus (or a prejudice) amongst communities about what has quality and what does not. Marks and Spencer are commonly named as producers of quality goods and services. However, if your requirements are modified because your purposes change, your perception of quality will shift and may influence your purchasing of goods from alternative suppliers. In this case, your perception of the quality of their goods is transformed solely because your requirements change.

Techniques already exist which provide feedback on the quality of services. Your agency could be using some of these techniques to develop an understanding of effectiveness. The important point here is that you have no need to create elaborate systems to monitor ongoing effectiveness. Here are some examples of systems and techniques which give feedback on quality services:

Patient questionnaires
Staff questionnaires
Patients' Charter monitoring
Patient and staff suggestion systems
Comments and complaints systems
Clinical audit
Departmental audits
Outcome monitoring systems
Feedback from Community Health Councils
Public health report monitoring systems

(see THE OUTCOME), page 73

Think about quality and how you can learn more about the quality of what you and your care agency achieve using these feedback systems. They should help you understand the perspective of the service user, who may see your activity as only a part of their services. Thinking about quality from the service user's point of view helps you remember that quality community care services do not happen by themselves. They come about because people working in positive organisational cultures make them happen.

Though it could be said that the people are the organisation, it is also true that the organisation is more than the people in it. Each organisation develops its own internal culture and outlook which provides the pulse and distinctive character of its internal activities and external relationships. Each organisation has a life of its own where it continually balances its contributions between those which fulfil its objectives and those which preserve its existence. Each must maintain this balance.

The Organisation

THE IMPORTANCE OF BEING PURPOSEFUL

QUESTIONS are tools for wrestling information and attitudes out onto open ground. They can help you learn about the range of perspectives which exist within your own agency. It would be naive to assume that every colleague sees the agency and what they do in clear and commonly agreed terms. Questioning gives you the opportunity to find your own clarity in what you are doing.

Some questions are dangerous. These questions are lethal weapons indeed, and should be used with caution and after much practice in relatively safe situations.

All three questions work on two levels. In one way they simply seek information. But in a more profound way they create conditions where the person being questioned must turn away from the processes, the agency's activities, to the more fundamental consideration of what the agency exists to achieve.

Here is the first of the three perilous questions:

ORGANISATION QUESTION 1
What is the purpose of this organisation?

You may ask this of colleagues who feel might find it difficult to appreciate the importance of organisational purpose. They may see the agency in terms of activity and are likely to respond with a "doing" answer.

Some people may become defensive, either because they have never thought in terms of purpose or because they suspect your simple question is "loaded". Your question is indeed loaded, and their responses will tell you more about how the agency functions than many an internal audit!

Hopefully others will be clear that the purpose of their community care agency is to achieve benefits for their service users. If they can identify what those benefits might be, it is likely that they have played an active part in the agency's effectiveness. They will have come to understand that purpose is the central unifying force of any successful enterprise. Purpose brings people, their skills and resources together to achieve an outcome which is perceived to be a benefit to their consumers. Even

11

wider-ranging and somewhat emotionally laden answers are likely in response to the second dangerous question, so it may be wise to make sure the first dangerous question has had time to prepare others for this one, which is:

ORGANISATION QUESTION 2

What is the purpose of what you are doing within the organisation?

Dynamite to some; absolutely straightforward to others. In asking this question, you will not be wanting the information that is usually contained in job descriptions. These largely relate to processes, not purpose. Asking people what they do is not the same as asking them the purpose of what they do! You will be asking them again to take the journey away from the day to day processes and locate themselves and their work in relation to the overall purpose of the agency. Some people may become resistant and others may have other difficulties, but with your help people may find their responses useful to themselves as well as to you.

The third dangerous question is one which is so seldom asked that a response may not be immediate. That question is:

ORGANISATION QUESTION 3

How do the people in this organisation learn?

Here you will be exploring whether the agency is forward thinking or simply reactive. You will be able to determine whether the forward thinking sectors of the organisation have an influence on the essentially reactive quarters and the nature of that influence. An agency which is active in its learning is usually able to identify its most effective learning patterns and techniques. Such an agency establishes and nurtures a learning culture in which successes and failures are both opportunities for learning. The learning culture is one which regularly addresses the question of purpose, its relevance and its achievability. When the defined purpose changes, the agency's business changes and the new learning required is likely to be considerable.

PURPOSE – THE INTENDED ACHIEVEMENT

Purpose is more about what an agency wants to achieve and less about how it achieves it. It is sometimes expressed in an agency's "mission statement" as a declaration of the overall goal of their activity. It is important to be clear that goals relate to the overall and ultimate purpose of an organisation, while objectives relate to the achievements that need to be in place before the purpose can be realized.

Purpose, important though it is, exists within a context of influences within an agency. Think of PURPOSE only existing in the company of others as a cluster of interdependent concepts. You must now come to terms with these concepts! These are the terms as used in this chapter and the rest of this book:

VISION – the potential
an imaginative but realistic insight into the possibility of future enhancements in the quality of life of service users and carers

PURPOSE – the intended outcome
a statement describing what is to be achieved for and with users of the service to enable them to participate in that future

VALUES or PRINCIPLES – the operational perspective
a series of statements which identify the agency's beliefs concerning the methods of achieving the PURPOSE

POLICY – the operational foundation
the coming together of **VISION, PURPOSE,** and **VALUES** to form a comprehensive statement of operational values to be employed and objectives to be achieved in the realization of the PURPOSE

STRATEGY – the map, the timetable, and the rules of engagement
a plan which sets values and objectives against timescales which are agreed to provide the most efficient itinerary for achieving the PURPOSE

STANDARDS – measuring the agency's activity (outputs)
statements of good practice which provide criteria for assessing the effectiveness of the agency's structures and processes in the realization of PURPOSE.

Purpose provides direction for these interdependent concepts which, in turn, reinforce organisational activities, informing and building on them. Purpose remains entirely dependent on the vision that is created by imaginative forward thinking about the possibilities for services. Without this imaginative but practical forecasting of what the future might look like for your service users, and a creative projection of what that might mean for your services and the way you commission or provide them, purpose remains hollow and uninspiring.

A clear idea of purpose provides the single most powerful benefit to your agency and the people associated with the agency; it clarifies the ultimate measure of success. How else will you get information about how well you are doing unless it comes from the achievement of clear objectives required for the realization of purpose?

Maintaining a clear focus on purpose excludes wasteful digressions and thereby reduces the risk of failure. Aiming explicitly and selectively at one or just a few targets excludes other possible goals and this conserves energy for achieving your purpose.

Secondly, purpose provides a focus for "systems design". The stitching together of processes and procedures related directly to the outcome the agency is intending to achieve. This means that you will engage in fewer practices which are unrelated to outcome because procedures are programmed to be interdependent for the achievement of the purpose.

Purpose has a central role both in providing the focus for quality services and providing the right sort of information for judging the quality of those services. But describing how to achieve purpose in personal care services is, by itself, not enough to fully describe quality personal care services. Achieving quality in personal services is not only a matter of achieving purpose. Quality is wider than purpose!

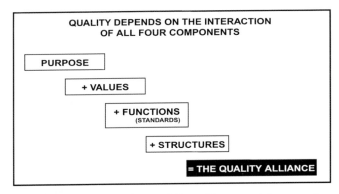

Quality is a product of the alliance of four major organizational activities:
purpose, values, functions, and structures.

Purpose and values are defined above as:

PURPOSE – a statement describing what is to be achieved for and with users of the service to enable them to participate in the future identified in the vision and

VALUES – a series of statements of good practice which identify the agency's beliefs concerning the most effective way of achieving the purpose.

To these we need to add:-

FUNCTIONS – the range of activities and tasks in which the agency engages to achieve objectives which eventually realize purpose

and

STRUCTURES – the organisational, physical and professional resources and their relationships necessary for the achievement of purpose.

These four aspects of organisational life form the alliance for quality. Think of these in a hierarchical relationship to each other:

✳ Purpose provides a focus for what is to be achieved by the agency's activity

✳ Values identify the manner in which the agency carries out those activities (functions)

* Functions identify what activities will achieve the agency's purpose

* Structures are designed to facilitate the activities which achieve the agency's purpose.

Together these four elements define the quality of the achievements of the agency. Change one element, and the others require reassessment and possibly redefinition. Simply tampering with organisational structures, for instance, will give incomplete results and be unsuccessful. Worse, it will be likely to lead to further restructuring if you fail to identify the effect of structural change on activity, on the values behind it and on the purpose as supported by the agency's values.

It is particularly important in personal services that the range of activities (functions) within health and social care contribute to the wellbeing of the user through worthwhile human contact. How personal services are provided is as important as the services themselves. This is why quality oriented organisations endeavour to establish standards which can be used in measuring the interpersonal processes that are always involved in community care. These standards address the quality of aspects of the service (e.g., "the services you receive from us will be reviewed with you every six months"), but they should also gauge the quality of the interpersonal processes involved in their provision (e.g., "your enquiry or complaint will be taken seriously and be treated in confidence by qualified or experienced people"). Standards, in the business of health and social care, are simply statements of good practice (function) which can be measured. It often seems easier to measure quantity than to measure quality, and that is why organisations have saddled their quality assurance managers with the monitoring of standards on waiting times, waiting lists, and any number of duration-based scales. We will see later that collecting qualitative information can be as easy as collecting quantitative data. It's not difficult, only different! (See THE OUTCOMES, page 73)

VALUES – THE CATALYST OF QUALITY CARING

Values are statements of good practice which identify the beliefs of people, their cultures or their organisations. Personal values somehow appear inborn and only somewhat fashioned by personal experience. Most often they are "understood" or even taken for granted and assumed. They are seldom written down and exposed to others because they are taken to be a very private matter. So private that, in everyday life, people would find saying what they believe in simple language a thoughtful and intricate task. So it is easier to assume that other people are like ourselves, believing the same things we believe, thinking similar benevolent thoughts.

Test this out for yourself. Use the margin to write five 1 values you hold personally. Write each in one complete sentence. Do it now, and time yourself to see how long it 2 takes you to get your five sentences!

If that took you less that 15 minutes, take yourself out to 3 a nice lunch. If it took you less than 5 minutes, get the boss to pay for the lunch! Most people would find this hard work, 4 and that means a few of you will be eating in today!

This personal approach to values tends to overflow into 5 the realms of work and professional practice. Groups of skilled professionals could quite possibly work shoulder to shoulder for years without realizing that the differences in their approach to the work may not be solely accounted for by influences of personality, training or experience. These are important differences that can, as we will see, represent a considerable asset to your organisation. But different approaches can also be based on the fundamentally dissimilar values which each worker brings to the organisation. This is why it is essential that organisations invest the time and energy required to **make explicit the values they hold.** Each agency and each team should negotiate five or so group held values. Only when they are identified, out in the open and vulnerable to scrutiny, do they become useful for the development of quality services.

Values provide the adhesive which binds the processes and functions of the organisation to its purpose. They demonstrate or embody the culture of the organisation. Not only are they statements which identify how one agency differs from another, but they are statements which make demands, particularly when applied to personal health and social care agencies. Because the business of these agencies is personal care, the values take on a "people first" character, prompting a more complex decision making perspective that is not simple. Values are a key element in establishing a culture for quality within the organisation.

Beware the pitfalls when identifying values. Creditable values are characterised by both their usefulness and their relevance. Good values make demands! Unfortunately statements which make no demands are often seen as values. In fact, they are little more than pious aspirations or sometimes sham pretences to credibility.

Comparing three types of value statements can help make this clear.

Useless Values— pious statements which make no demands:

> We want the best for you
> We want to help you be happy
> We will always listen to you
> You are important to us
> Your independence is our main concern

Irrelevant Values – statements which say more about attitudes than beliefs:

> We will help you understand the problems we have in working within the NHS
> You can refuse our services at any time for any reason
> Your appreciation of our professional expertise is important to us
> Younger people have more potential for change than older people
> We help older people accept change

Model values for the caring services should be useful and relevant. They should be statements of ideas of worth in themselves, and should be useful to the achievement of the agency's purpose.

Model Values – statements which inform and make demands

> Service users will have the greatest possible control over their own lives and personal privacy
> Service users have the right to make informed decisions about personal risk-taking provided that other people are not disadvantaged or endangered
> We recognize that people may require assistance and time to understand fully the implications of their disabilities

We consult regularly with groups of service users and carers about the effectiveness of our services and the development of new services
We encourage people to tell us when things go wrong and invite them to identify their own spokesperson to assist them if required.

Values are the substructure for organisational functioning.

FUNCTIONS – THE ACTIVITY OF CARING

Functions are the everyday activities that contribute to the achievement of purpose. They are the range of operations and tasks through which the agency illustrates its values in achieving its aims. The hands-on caring, the support and guidance and the strategic planning are all activities which should be performed in harmony in the pursuit of common objectives.

Functions are the means and not the end. They have no meaning outside the context of purpose. Often care workers have a good enough idea as to why they do what they do, but without giving much thought to what they anticipate they will achieve. When standards are set only to ensure that functions achieve a minimum uniformity, they fail to reflect the actual effectiveness of the function. If standards are set in this way it is usually a sign that the agency is confusing its activities with its purpose. Remember, the purpose of your agency is to achieve something, not simply to do something to a given standard. Meeting the standard and achieving the outcome are two very different things.

Functions are, of course, essential to any service agency, but they are not of such central importance as purpose. They have their place in the quality alliance only inasmuch as they serve the achievement of purpose.

Standards exist only in relation to functions. By themselves, standards are not quality! They make a contribution – an important one – to quality outcomes. When good standards are being met there is an acknowledgement of consistency, and that in itself is important. Quality usually cannot happen without the stability that consistent functioning provides. Do not let yourself think that standards represent quality. By themselves, standards make statements about consistency, not quality.

In setting standards for community care functions it will be necessary to reflect your agency's purpose and values.

For this reason it is essential that standard setting is a collaborative activity across all relevant managerial and operational levels within the agency. Small standard setting groups are likely to develop more appropriate and comprehensive standards than a single professional working alone. Standards make the agency's understanding of its task explicit and should be publicised so that they can help your agency and its service users measure how well you are doing.

Standards are important for five reasons:

* Standards improve clarity of purpose and function

* Standards translate policy into practice

* Standards can improve the quality of outcomes by encouraging the service user to participate

* Standards create expectations of staff and service users clear and therefore

* Standards improve efficiency.

Standards are simply statements of good practice which have some element of measurability within them. This measurability factor we shall call the "M Factor". Standards are also examples of good practice which can serve as instruments for evaluating services and performance. Standards serve to tell others what they can expect from the agency staff, and make clear to staff what is expected of them.

There are three types of standards, and it is important that each standard setting group is agreed about which type of standards it is identifying. To mix them is to confuse the whole objective of standard setting. The type chosen will depend on many factors, such as skills available, economic climate, local political realities, or policy directives.

1 Ideal Standards
If you decide to set ideal standards, your group will be identifying the ultimate in good practice with little reference to the economic or political atmosphere. It is then essential that members of the team share the same values and are prepared to put forward an articulate case to persuade others that ideal standards should be the agreed targets. Be prepared for those others not to agree, and plan how to

manage their resistance (see CHANGE AND RESISTANCE, page 47). Also be prepared for negotiations about ideal standards to take time.

2 Minimum Standards

In setting minimum standards you will be defining baseline performance – that least level of performance which is required to achieve "good-enough" practice. This may be the best choice if you are bringing together agencies which have little or no shared concept of good practice, or which are unfamiliar with quality management initiatives. These statements represent the minimum level of professional practice; below this level the work is unacceptable to the team members and the agencies involved.

3 Optimal Standards

These standards are statements of what you judge to be the best achievable good practice within existing economic, organisational or political constraints. They may be your choice when the team is prepared to move beyond the baseline minimum when looking for performance targets. They demand a thoroughly realistic appraisal of the culture within which the services will operate.

Once the decision is made about which type of standard to set, the work can begin on developing statements of good practice. Remember, it is essential that there be an element of measurability in each statement. It can either measure achievement of the outcome directly or the processes involved in achieving that outcome. So, if the standard states that each service user will have a copy of their personal service plan within one week of its completion, the "M Factor" (one week) directly measures the outcome (the service user having a copy of the plan). If a standard states that each service plan will be reviewed every three months, the "M Factor" (three months) is seen to measure a process (service review) rather than an outcome. Some standards will identify outcomes to be achieved, whilst others may relate to the processes involved. Others may address both. Standards should deal with both outcomes and processes because quality is not only a matter of achieving the desired outcome. Quality means achieving it in a way which is positively acceptable to the service user.

STRUCTURE –
THE FRAMEWORK OF THE ORGANISATION

Structure underpins the achievement of organisational purpose by supporting value-based functions. When purpose, values and functions are less well understood, organisations tend to become preoccupied with their own structures. Drives for increased productivity (more functions) or efficiency (more functions per budget unit) often form the content of these preoccupations!

Structural changes occur as a response to new legislation and professional ideological changes in belief as to what are the most appropriate forms of care services (e.g. home care vs residential care). However, the many and often repeated re-structuring activities have been responses either to changes in funding or "clarifications" of political ideology without funding adjustments to meet newly identified implications. Both provide pressure for a change in structure – often called re-configuration or re-engineering – and signal the start of an activity that seems solely and completely involved with the underpinnings of the organisation. Tamperings in insufferable committee rooms create the same effect as removing the bottom soup tin in the supermarket stack! One or two restructures weaken but don't topple the stack, but at some stage the removal of the critical component will bring collapse. The whole business begins to tilt and become unstable as those appointed to meddle with the foundations generate "solutions" that do not build on each other. Structural changes brought about to deal with financial pressures or managerial problems do not generally contribute to the holistic wellbeing of the agency. They are usually high theatre, strong on reformation, but weak on resolution.

Clearly what should happen is the reverse: the initial concerns should be about how change in funding or function affect the stated purpose of the organisation. If the purpose remains intact, then it may be necessary to look toward a change in organisational values. Given that these remain stable, you must then look toward adjusting the functions to meet the requirements of change. Then finally the structure could be amended to support the functions and safeguard the first two elements. Looking to the structure first because it presents easily identifiable targets produces short term solutions and long term problems which are usually at the expense of quality.

ORGANISATIONAL TYPE AND CULTURE

No two organisations are the same. No single organisation is the same from one year to the next. There is always change, but usually within boundaries set by the organisation's perception of itself and its business. If the purpose of the agency is to provide community care housing, employment opportunities, or day care services, it will be primarily interested in its **activity.** If its purpose is to empower disadvantaged or devalued people to improve the quality of their own lives by providing these services, the **achievement** of empowered living becomes the focus.

Organisations were not created to behave in the way that they often do; they evolve. They develop a history that can be a strong enabler or prohibitor of good things happening. It is important to understand what kind of organisation you work with or within, and essential to understand its operating culture. Do the operating cultures of the agencies you work with for better community care services promote or inhibit progress toward that common goal?

Here are four classic kinds of organisation to consider. Any organisation may operate in one or more of these styles, and remember that in trying to understand an organisation you are collecting basic information so as to improve it, not condemn it.

1 The Controlling Organisation
This type of agency is often hierarchical and authoritarian. Decision-taking is centralised and those decisions often seem politically influenced.

2 The Functional Organisation
Here is an organisation completely focused on its own processes. Many rules and systems dominate working practice, and staff can become more threatened by failed procedures than failed outcomes. Often externally or politically motivated, the emphasis here is on striving for error free performance.

3 The Achievement Organisation
Internally motivated and outcome oriented, this is an agency where the commonly shared objectives and tasks are well understood by staff and partner agencies. Processes and activities are only important in so far as they relate to the final outcome. Decisions are taken by the people with the information required to take them, irrespective of hierarchical position.

4 The Sustaining Organisation
This organisation reflects the internal relationships of its staff and often finds structures which accentuate the interdependence required for staff to meet the common goal. Procedures are seldom isolated in one part of the organisation. Activity links various professionals together as a team for achieving the common goal.

These four descriptions by themselves do not differentiate good and bad organisations. They only provide a backdrop for your consideration so that you can understand your organisation better. They help you appreciate why it functions so well in some areas and so poorly in others.

Most organisations are likely to demonstrate elements of one or another kind, making them hybrids of the four types identified here. This implies that organisations function in any number of ways. How they do function is a matter of culture. So, against the possible kinds of organisation there is a range of operational behaviours, or cultures. Identifying these will enhance your understanding of how your agency works. Here are five for your consideration.

1 Systems Culture
The activity is of the utmost importance in this culture. The best workers are seen to be those who do the most. The task has also to be performed in the correct fashion, so procedures are usually well defined particularly where the agency feels most vulnerable to criticism (e.g. access to its services, assessment). A place for everything and everything in its place! Where there is a hierarchical structure it is likely to be tall with each level difficult to access from two tiers below. The culture is one of control where middle managers feel inclined to say "No!" first. These agencies

are generally characterized by very limited personal relatedness and the inability of front line staff to influence decision making.

2 Personal Pathological Culture
The agency that blames! Very preoccupied with political acceptability and devotes a high level of energy and resources to rooting out the causes of mistakes or embarrassment. Fault finding is a generalist skill in this organisation, and where problems are identified they often are designated by a staff member's name (or former staff member). "That is a problem because that's Joe's team, and you know what they are like!" Power and punishment games abound as groups within the organisation redefine problems as someone else's responsibility.

3 The "On Your Bike" Culture
These agencies are highly competitive but often demonstrate poor creativity. The atmosphere is highly charged and the participants feel part of a life and death struggle simply to hold on to their jobs. If you don't perform to very high and often undefined standards it is time to think about your future! Glossy marketing material is there to create the illusion that achievements are greater than they often are.

4 Crisis Culture
This agency operates without vision or plans. Policies are developed in response to procedural problems arising. Therefore priorities change too often to be defined usefully. This agency is largely reactive and seldom takes a leading position. It is strong in problem solving capability, low on strategic thinking. The message is that the agency prefers working hard to working intelligently. This is often a characteristic of organisations where the political leadership is split or over-reactive to perceived ideological demands.

5 Learning Culture
An agency which continues to learn is always changing because it continually takes in information about its performance and evaluates it. Here failure is recognized as valid learning and high regard is paid to its feedback mechanisms. High levels of personal relatedness ensure effective communication and this is reflected in communication

systems which augment the more traditional and less effective cascade system. High strategic thinking capability where service development is seen as a participative programme for all staffing levels within the agency is characteristic of learning cultures. All work is evaluated and decisions are made to refine working practices on the basis of those evaluations.

Organisational culture comes about through a succession of forces and reactions. It is often a product of political or financial attitudes to risk and can sometimes be a consequence of size. It is unlikely that any one organisation could be completely described by any one of the definitions above; they may have characteristics of three or four cultural models. Whatever the causes or complexity of organisational behaviour, understanding the type and culture of the organisations within which you spend your working life can empower you to develop effective skills which help the agency to achieve its community care purpose. That purpose is to assist vulnerable people to achieve a better quality of life for themselves or for the people they care for in the community.

This leaves you with four questions you should be able to answer at some point while you are reading this book:

What type of organisation do I work within?

What type of organisation should it be?

What is the culture of this organisation?

What should the culture be?

Mark or fold the corner of this page as you may have to come back to it at a later date. When you are able to answer these questions, you will have an idea about how much energy you will need to put into the process of getting the agency into shape. It may take some time, even years, and the chances are that you cannot do it on your own, so find those people who can also make a contribution. They may be very close to where you sit at work now! Have a look around. (See PLANNING, page 59)

**A WORD ABOUT
COMMUNICATION AND NETWORKING**

Communication is regularly identified as a malfunctioning area in many organisations. Where two or more people are gathered together, there is the opportunity for mis-communication! Communication, whatever its quality, provides the structure for the operational information required by any organisation. Where communication is poor, the ability of the organisation to function is limited. Unhappily, assumptions are made that communication in agencies is good enough because there is a logical communication system. You may have had experience where the communication system exists, but communication does not. Identify three or four of those experiences now in the margin.

Communication is essentially sharing. It is at least a two way process, and often multi-dimensional. It is the sharing of information, time, skills and commitment for achieving the common goal. Good communication assumes two pre-conditions:

1 Communicating parties share a common interest and a willingness to listen

2 Communicating parties recognise the importance of their various viewpoints and contributions.

Networking is an excellent method of communication. Good networking takes time and energy but is a powerfully effective tool for ensuring that the agency is acting as one and in accord with other organisations. Networking is defined simply as forming alliances for the benefit of service users. It thrives on the differences in the skills and perceptions of those involved in providing community care services. It understands these differences and respects them. Networking utilises those differences to enhance each agency's understanding of the complexity of the community care task.

Networking is the message of the NHS and Community Care Act. No one agency engineers the network. Networking cannot be "managed" wholly from the viewpoint of any single agency. Organisations which see themselves as central to the community care task often overlook this point and can be recognized by their over-concern with their own processes.

Most community care professionals network, but often only as a fringe activity. Networking is a major tool to be used in two modes: "in house" and "open house".

"In House Networking"
This is networking within your own organisation, and usually takes one of two forms:

Person-to-Person Networking — setting and communication of the agency's
goals, values and stan-
dards
— generating commitment
to the goals
— generating commitment
to the communication
process

Systemic Networking — use of information systems and technology to
achieve the agency's
goals
— strategic planning
— outcome monitoring

Person-to-person networking requires the context that systemic networking provides. Personal networking alone
often ends in dissipated energies, while systemic networking on its own is often unfocused.

"Open House" Networking
This is networking amongst the public and other community care agencies. Again it can be both person-to-person
or systemic, but outside the boundaries of your agency. As
with "in house" networking, both forms of networking are
required for success.

Communicating requires openness to others and a willingness to listen and learn. It is a broad and complex
subject and many pages are devoted to it in organisational
and managerial texts. For our purposes here there are simply two rules to remember when you communicate:

**1 People (and agencies) communicate far more
non-verbally than they do through the spoken or
written word.**
About 70% of the content of human communication is
non- verbal, that is, looks, shrugs, or silences. People
get a message from you that may or may not be the
one you wish to send. You may need help from others
to understand what works for you and what does not
and practice to make the most of your non-verbal
abilities.

Non-verbal organisational messages are given
through goal setting processes. Policy gaps and poor

planning speak clearly to those who are alert and listening to the silences!

2 The cascade communication system does not work.
The biggest problem here is that it looks if it should work and many people believe it does work. It is convenient and apparently time efficient, but it is largely ineffective. Being efficiently ineffective scores no points! The problem is that the communication line down through the organisation usually follows the managerial line, and this already has natural filters built in, where personal interests (or lack of interest) screen both communication and feedback.

Cascade systems are so embedded in agencies that it is likely they will stay there unmoved, so put some thought to developing an "off line" method of communication which can augment, not replace this well established but relatively ineffective system. One model could be an identified person within the organisation reporting directly to the chief executive (and not in the management hierarchy) to take key issues to each tier of the management structure both to provide information and receive feedback.

Good communication helps the organisation respond to people.

The People

EMPOWERMENT TO THE PEOPLE

I T could be said that the purpose of health and social care services is to empower people who are disadvantaged or devalued or disabled to maintain or improve the quality of their own lives. If this is a true and useful statement, though clearly not an exhaustive one, it follows that empowerment is the business of health and social care in the community. Early attempts to provide community based services failed because they were characterised by professional practices more suited to the institutional culture. People who were disadvantaged because they required care were too often devalued by the very systems of care surrounding them. These systems have simply failed to engage the service user in a positive human way. In the past, an unintended lowering of the status of the service user had occurred during the subtle manoeuvres of "care" with the effect of actually promoting dependence. While people who need help are dependent, relatively few are totally dependent.

In short, the systems of care – and the caring itself – cannot be allowed to prevent service users having access to opportunities which help them improve the quality of their own lives.

To understand empowerment more fully, it is useful to think of it as linked stages of developing abilities, or capabilities. There are five stages in all, and as we will see later, they relate directly to four stages of the development of service user participation. The five stages are:

1   Developing the ability to **UNDERSTAND**

2   Developing the ability to **IDENTIFY WHAT NEEDS TO CHANGE**

3   Developing the ability to **CRITICIZE**

4   Developing the ability to **NEGOTIATE**

5   Developing abilities for better **SELF-MANAGEMENT**.

STAGE 1 Developing the ability to understand.

This is the foundation of empowerment. It is essential that service users have as complete an understanding as is useful to them of the conditions, the situations and the lifestyles that disadvantage, disable, devalue or demoralize them. Before they have that understanding, service users share no common ground from which to negotiate a better quality living experience for themselves. To gain this understanding they may have to confront what might be very painful realities about their past and current personal circumstances. For example, they may need to accept the prognosis of a longer term disability. Service users may simply need information both about their condition and what is available to help them manage.

The care professional may have to acclimatize to the service users' need for (and right to) information. Initially, it may mean being clear and explicit about the care professional's role and the capability of the organisation behind the professional to commission or provide services. Being clear about who is going to do what is a good start. But this could easily be extended into shared user files or even user-held records. Without information, the service user is disadvantaged.

There are two major obstacles to be overcome when sharing or providing information to patients or clients. The first of these is their low expectations of both themselves and the agencies they have come to rely on for assistance or guidance. This demonstrates itself in the passive but often grateful acceptance of the status quo. Professionals may need to invest energy in helping the users of the services to raise their expectations. Providing all the information to which the service user is entitled is the first essential step. Information presented personally in easily understandable formats helps service users who have low expectations to make more informed service requests, and encourages more purposeful service user participation.

The second obstacle exists within the care professional. This is the tendency to manage the response of the service user by withholding information. It sounds totally objectionable when described in this way, but it is an understandable (though inexcusable) reaction where professionals find themselves matching escalating demand for service with diminishing resources. Withholding information only serves to maintain the power of the service provider in a relationship which should be characterized by informed partnership.

The agency's assumption of the "right" to withhold information from service users is a powerful obstacle. It serves so well as a defence against the care worker's own feelings of frustration and inadequacy. It is particularly strong where the workers assume responsibility for the failures and inadequacies of their organisation. Professionals have been known to so successfully camouflage the withholding of information with good intentions toward the service user or loyalty to the agency that it is difficult to confront.

Withholding information about possible service alternatives protects the professionals, not the service users. Withholding information disempowers service users and undermines their ability to improve the quality of their own lives. It can be recognized, however, by asking the organisation and its workers this question: Do you withhold information about services or opportunities which would benefit the service user but that, because of financial or other constraints, you have no realistic hope of providing? If the answer is yes, it is likely that information is being withheld from the service users that may be useful in assisting them to improve the quality of their own lives. Uninformed people cannot make real choices; they can only pick from the selection you provide to them. This limits their rights and limits their ability to take control of their own lives (empowerment) In effect, it promotes continued inadequacy and frustration not only in service users but in the care workers who have, in fact, "managed" the information to allow only the "acceptable" information to be held outside the organisation.

The alternative, of course, is a full and honest presentation of the facts, with the care purchasers or provider neither taking responsibility for failures which are not their own nor "siding" with the service user against the agency. Protecting people from their own responses following their raised expectations is not the business of the professional. Recording the unmet need which may be identified in a more candid exchange during the assessment process is not only more empowering for the service user, it is a legal requirement of the NHS and Community Care Act.

Use the margins now to identify ways which you and your agency can assist service users to have information and to use it.

STAGE 2 Developing the ability to identify what needs to change

Informed people can make choices. They are able to develop a perspective about what would help them to improve the quality of their lives. They can learn not only what is not good enough for them, but also what needs to change and who needs to be influenced to help them effect that change. This is a powerful step forward for service users.

The activity of recognizing what requires change and who needs to be influenced reinforces, for service users, the unequal nature of their relationships with care agencies. The professionals control access to the resources, and however they approach their work in the spirit of equality, service user and professional are in no way equal in terms of what they bring to the relationship. They have different perspectives which ensure that this association is a partnership of inequalities, of differing skills and roles. Nevertheless, it can be a partnership with a commonly agreed aim, that is, the empowerment of the service user. In that way it shares common ground with most successful partnerships in that it brings together people with different skills to achieve an agreed outcome. Partnerships are built on differences, and it is the partnership's ability to access those differences within itself that makes for good teamwork. Creatures with the same skills and roles and maintaining similar approaches to doing what they do best are not partnerships or teams; they are more like flocks!

The empowered service user, therefore, has relatively limited authority within a working partnership with care agencies. Influence is the major way whereby the user can effect change. The ability to influence, the ability to bring about change without the direct responsibility for that change, can itself be misunderstood. Professionals who have failed to use their own influence within the agency to bring about change may interpret service users' attempts to influence them as manipulative or unrealistic. Worse still, the professional could label the service user's attempts to influence change as "understandable" in terms of the condition from which the service user suffers and, therefore, not to be taken seriously. In doing this the professional projects the agency bias against individual influence onto the service user. The reality is that the professional should interpret this use of influence as an indicator of the second stage of empowerment, the first being a developed understanding of the reality of the circumstances. Attempts to influence which are based on inadequate information will generally be a waste of time all round. People who know what they are talking about and what they want are most likely to be influential! The professional should acknowledge the service user's influence as a "powerful" ingredient with which to work.

Knowing what changes are necessary offers the first point of discussion between professionals and those they serve. It offers positive and continuing dialogue about why the partnership exists in the first place. It represents the first and lasting practical interaction following the development of understanding.

Recognizing who needs to be influenced to effect the desired change represents a powerful step forward for service users. The key agencies and professionals have to be identified before one can ensure that they are listening. Empowering agencies will ensure that service users know which people carry responsibilities for decisions relating to resources as well as overall policy.

Now, identify three or four practical ways you and your agency can help service users identify for themselves what they would like to change in their lives. Again, use the margins.

STAGE 3 Developing the ability to criticize

Criticizing is not something most of us find easy to do because it has overtones of disharmony and conflict. However, it is essential to the process of empowerment that the skill of effective critical input be cultivated. Criticism follows naturally from developing an understanding of what is not good enough and identifying what you should change to improve or resolve a situation.

Criticism both makes people vulnerable in the giving and is difficult in the receiving. People will often go to enormous lengths to bar the way for others to criticize them. There is a whole world of defensive behaviour against criticism, and with a little thought over a quiet lunch most of us could (reluctantly) identify the ways we block from people telling us what they need to tell us and what we need to hear.

Some professionals are so closely bound to their organisation or its traditions that its failures become their failures.

The possibility of allowing and encouraging honest criticism in this case can seem doubly difficult. Criticism of the agency then becomes criticism of the professionals themselves. Criticism of the agency then becomes profoundly uncomfortable for the professionals, and there is no safe refuge from personal criticism.

Other professionals can remain too detached from their agency and become defended against any personal or professional criticism. Any criticism is easily passed on to the organization itself. The message in response to any criticism is clear: "I'm OK! You're OK! THEY are the problem!" Whilst fearing being blamed some care professionals find themselves looking for someone or something else to blame.

Criticism need not fall into rudeness nor should it require excessive planning and preparation. Effective criticism makes its point without making enemies. You can identify problems without laying blame or making people feel inadequate. It is a skill amongst a number of assertive abilities that you could employ to raise issues rather than tempers or defences. The art of criticism is developed by practice, both in the receiving and the giving.

Think now of how you react to criticism of something you have done. Do you feel more vulnerable when you are criticized or when you criticize others? When was the last time you criticized poor professional practice directly to the person responsible?

STAGE 4 Developing the ability to negotiate

Negotiation is simply the process of bargaining to reach a mutually acceptable agreement. It is the process whereby service users engage in the planning of their care to achieve what they want for themselves. Empowered negotiation is really about service users haggling for more control, more freedom, and more ownership of the care and support they receive from the agencies. Negotiation is the fourth stage of empowered living and is likely to lead to successful self-management when service users become their own care managers!

Negotiation is learned through practice. It can either be competitive, where the style is confrontational and success is seen in terms of winners and losers; or collaborative, where the atmosphere is more one of working toward a common goal and success is judged by the level of satisfaction achieved by both parties. Such negotiations demonstrate contrasting emphases:

COMPETITIVE	COLLABORATIVE
Winners and losers	Joint winners
Hold out for desired outcome	Attempt to achieve mutually satisfactory outcome
Tough-mindedness	Clear-mindedness
Problem identification	Problem avoidance
Intimidation	Endorsement
Brinkmanship	Conflict management
Stating the position	Listening

In relationships where power is vested differentially amongst the parties (as it is in personal care situations) either kind of negotiation could be employed. In practice, competitive negotiation is likely to reward the more powerful, whilst the collaborative negotiating method is likely to be more equitable.

Identify how you and your agency negotiate with service users. Are services negotiated, or only offered on a "take it or leave it" basis? How can you develop better negotiation skills for yourself and for your service user?

STAGE 5 Developing abilities for self-management

Self-management is not to be confused with independence. Self-management is the capability of actively showing the responsibility one has for one's own life. It is, in fact, the opposite of institutionalized behaviour, whether the factors encouraging dependency occur as a result of care systems or are an outcome of support by "caring" relatives or community provided facilities. The fact that one is unable to maintain a relatively high level of independence is in itself no justification for others to take control and responsibility for organizing the support and care required.

Each of us is dependent on others for the most basic needs in our society, and only an extraordinarily small number of people achieve the highest levels of independent behaviour. Yet most of us are quite capable of managing our lives within the range of activities we allow ourselves along the continuum of independence. This broad area is called the interdependence zone, in which most people find themselves. In terms of population, the continuum is likely to look like this:

Dependence **<Interdependence>** Independence

The ability to self-manage is not only a matter of developing practical skills, though individual skills relating to medication, personal care and budgeting prolong one's stay within the interdependent zone. Equally important is the ability to achieve a level of emotional wellbeing to sustain a person over longer periods of time. Emotional wellbeing is the positive state which is characterised by a person's ability to remain resilient in response to life's good and bad news. This resilience has the effect of stabilizing the person's reactions to circumstances or events which have a personal impact.

No one is born into a state of emotional wellbeing. Every person must learn to adjust to new situations from the earliest moments, and in this way becomes more capable of acting in the world as they find it. It is a competence which is learned in stages, first in situations which are not so extreme as to overwhelm one's ability to respond appropriately.

Emotional wellbeing is not a dispassionate state, an inability to feel or understand the personal implications of life's events. This is simply detachment, an emotional disability producing a rigidity of response which can be mistaken for stability and strength.

Emotionally healthy people are able to feel anger, to be stirred by passion, to experience love, hate, envy, sorrow, joy and zeal in ways that are self-motivating, and not self-limiting. They take risks because they have an inner vitality that can cope with failure and rejection. They have learned to engage with what their world has presented to them and survive!

THE DEVELOPMENT OF THE PERSON THROUGH PARTICIPATION

The five levels of empowerment cannot be achieved without some personal growth and development on the part of the carer and cared-for. Honest participation in the planning and provision of community care services requires skills and promotes capabilities which promote the empowerment process.

There are two important principles sustaining the process of change through participation. Empowerment through participation rest on these two simple truths:

1 **People are more likely to change when _they_ have identified the need for change**

2 **People are more likely to accept change when they are involved in the processes of change.**

Participation of service users and their carers develops in four stages which approximately mirror the empowerment stages (above). It is not simply a matter of consulting service users. Consultation is only the first stage, not the last! The four stages are:

1 Consultation
2 Collaboration
3 Negotiation
4 Self-management

1 Consultation
Consultation is the first stage toward full user participation and often the first step to empowerment. It is the elementary communication in which information is given (monologue) or shared (dialogue). It is the stage where definitions are made clear and common understandings are developed. Successful consultation is fundamentally a matter of the quality of communication; it is not about achieving agreement. It is the stage where a modicum of trust can be developed and where all participants can develop some confidence in the process of communication, if not yet in the communicators themselves!

2 Collaboration
This next stage of user participation builds on the confidence developed in the previous stage. Here are the beginnings of shared responsibility for service planning and monitoring. In collaboration, commissioners, providers and representatives of the users of services develop the critical thinking capabilities that are necessary for determining the effectiveness of community care. Collaboration assumes that information is available in understandable formats to all those involved in the care services. Client held records, open forum public meetings and planning partnerships with service user groups are steps in the right direction. It is

likely that these initiatives will require support and training for service users and carers so that their participation can be both informed and effective.

3 Negotiation
Building on the confidence established in the collaboration stage where responsibilities for planning and monitoring are shared, this third stage marks the establishment of representation, where the rights and wishes of service users are formally represented and the principle of independent advocacy taken more fully into the commissioning processes. Here is the acknowledgement of the right of all participants to say "No!" It is at this stage that commissioning agencies could establish initiatives for sharing their purchasing power with those who have a clearer understanding of what they require from the services purchased; that is, the service users and their carers.

4 Self-management
Self-management is the goal of any care in the community service, and is the ultimate indicator for successful user participation programmes. In time, this could mean that commissioning agencies act more as specialist assessors or enablers, with most of the funding for services being made available directly to the service users or their representatives. For all but the most dependent, self-management means that each service user becomes his or her own care manager!

THE EMPOWERING PEOPLE

Those who empower must understand what it means to be empowered. Empowered people radiate an honest confidence with high levels of personal sensitivity to the needs of others. They have experience of taking more responsibility and control of what they do. They know that no one person can empower another directly, but they can work together with service users to create the conditions that encourage people to take more responsibility for their lives and for what they achieve.

Community care can be an intensely personal experience both for the service user and the service provider. It is the quality of this personal relationship that is most important to those who for any reason must rely on the help of others to sustain themselves and remain in control of their lives. The agency staff, the care assessors or care managers, and the home care assistants and other providers of services work as a team of people, not as robots, bureaucrats or functionaries. To achieve the most for the service user, they must develop capabilities which themselves demonstrate interdependence within the team as a model for interdependent living.

All five stages of empowerment and all four stages of user participation apply to the professional staff who work together as part of the service user's team. The challenge they face, however, is different. They are likely to be free from the weakening effects of chronic illness or disability. However, health and social care agency staff must negotiate another hurdle along the way toward personal empowerment: the agency itself! The agency will, from time to time, change the way it sees its role and this has implications for how it achieves the new goals it sets for itself. Unfortunately, recent history demonstrates that this "change of vision" is almost exclusively a matter for senior managers, who necessarily take a highly focused view of the agency as it adapts to the political and economic changes we have come to expect. This leads to change which is largely "top-down" and results in communication difficulties as each level within the organisation may have a very different understandings of vision and purpose.

Intelligent and effective survival through change is more likely when the whole of the care agency works together with its service users to ensure that the agency's purpose and the quality of the outcomes achieved remain intact and relevant. The stability that staff seek during times of change must be integrated with the very processes of change, and not stand as an alternative state. Staff who have developed more effective participation in the change process are more able to influence that change. These staff members have learned that there is no satisfaction in being victims of change.

ASSERTIVENESS

You as a care professional need to engage with your agency in ways which always promote the achievement of the agency's purpose. Your assertive behaviour should be seen as an indicator of an enlightened response rather than a threat within the agency.

Assertion is simply saying (or showing) what should be said, at the right time, to the right people and in the most useful way. Being assertive often requires a "leap of faith" because assertive exchanges are largely alien to established communication customs. Also, unknown consequences may result from unusual communication experiences. Being assertive means that you take a chance in harmlessly demonstrating your strength of feeling or opinion with clarity and honesty. See assertiveness as a gift to the agency! Being assertive is another way of giving.

Assertiveness is an effective way of giving information, though it is not the only way. Rather than a threat, assertive behaviour can offer the opportunity for clarity which is required from time to time during the processes of change. To see it as threatening is to generate fear that impedes personal or organisational abilities to manage change.

Fear is the initial and universal response to threat. It raises anxiety which can provide temporary strength to manage dangers. Fear provides a helpful warning that empowers us to protect ourselves and survive.

Fear can provide the energy to free us from threats or it can render us frozen and unable to act. The frightened lion attacks: the frightened rabbit waits in the headlights. Fear is a strong force in our culture, but it can play out its disabling ways too easily when communication is restricted by design or custom. Three kinds of fear restrict communication.

1 Fear of the loss of control

There is the possibility that your feelings can be strong and cause loss of control and, therefore, of effectiveness. Effectiveness depends on control, to be sure, but also depends on forcefulness. There is a need to balance these two elements. "Letting go" with control and directing communication toward those who need to know and who have the power and ability to improve things can be a very positive change agent.

2 Fear of becoming angry

If you are frightened of becoming angry, the chances are that you are already angry and don't feel safe enough to admit it. Fear and anger are so closely linked! Fearful exchanges are most likely to be angry ones.

3 Fear of getting it wrong and looking foolish

You don't have to be an expert to have an opinion, even a strongly held opinion. Strong opinions can be positive forces for change. However, it is not useful to identify yourself too closely with your opinion so that it cannot change without you being personally humiliated.

Assertive behaviour is directed where it will do the most good and can successfully challenge the unexpressed fears identified above. Expressing frustration by kicking the cat, throwing a dish, or scoring points off colleagues behind their backs only provides temporary entertainment. Sadly this undirected "letting go" can become a way of life within agencies and at best release only sufficient energy to allow participants to re-engage with the frustration after the moment passes. This resolves nothing. How much better it is to direct the energy toward the causes of the conflict which support your frustration.

Directing your assertive exchanges toward those who need to know and who have the power or responsibility to bring about change can bring the right forces to bear on those conditions within the agency which are unacceptable.

Your emotionally expressed responses which are not emotionally overladen are often your most effective. They are less exhausting and easier to deliver if the atmosphere of fear within you agency is reduced. This reduction is not achieved through managerial edict alone. It is a team effort, where team members overcome their fears of becoming emotionally exposed by demonstrating tolerance and taking chances with the tolerance of others. Knowing which emotions work for you personally and which do not is a great help, too. Self knowledge and self discipline encouraged by good personal support systems can build your confidence and diminish your fears.

People are sometimes reluctant to voice conflicting or alternative views because they feel others are better informed or in an organisational position which connotes a "special knowledge". The fact is that often it is the simple straightforward question which has the most powerful effect. Simple questions have the power to refocusing attention on fundamental concepts. Simple questions like, "How does what we are doing now contribute to achieving our objectives?" are often posed by non-experts. You do not have to be an expert to participate assertively, and many times it is important that you are not an expert. Non-experts are refreshingly jargon-free, and their questions require clear responses without the assumed subtext of "expertise."

Fear of exposure and vulnerability is a common and understandable feeling and is a natural component of any assertion. The anxiety raised in pointed disagreement or persistent pursuit of clarification is a motivator to successful communication. This is why assertive techniques need to be practised in personal situations outside work as well as at work. Opportunities to practice assertion happen at home, in the supermarket, in restaurants and in traffic jams. Rehearse first in safer situations. Try dropping off the apologetic introductions to your questions, such as "I'm sorry, but...." The next time you are ready to say "I'm sorry, but I don't understand what you are talking about!", try "I'm trying to understand you! Please explain....." With enough practice you will become comfortable with the fundamental law of assertiveness:

The assertive person is more vulnerable than those receiving the assertive message.

Without practice, we may well find it easy to confuse assertiveness with power-playing or offensiveness. It is neither of these things. It is simply making the point that you need to make, to the right people, at the right time and in the most effective way.

Healthy and effective assertiveness is about control. Anger, strong feelings, and even aggression can amplify the effect of communication and raise the quality of debate as long as the issue – the message – remains central. At times, there is nothing so productive as well focused anger to make the point effectively. Rehearsing assertiveness helps us learn to use our power without fear.

EMPOWERING PEOPLE TO EMPOWER OTHERS

Community care professionals who experience the benefits of self esteem are more likely to encourage services users to develop skills which help them feel good about themselves. Agencies which provide services to vulnerable people in the community must commit themselves to demonstrating empowered living if their staff are to cultivate empowered behaviour. The personal relationship between the service user and the care provider is the medium through which empowered living comes about. Professional staff in agencies work in teams, and it is in this context that empowerment is learnt and understood. How can teams of workers who are often random work groupings take on the empowerment culture? Competent management is a good start. Every team and every work group demonstrates a range of skills and personalities that are unique to itself. A good manager will understand this and set out to help each team member gain real satisfaction from their efforts because this is the best way of ensuring they return the highest quality work.

Managers can understand their teams in terms of the types of people as well as in terms of the skills each person brings to the team. Here are five types of team managers to consider: the Five "Ps" in teams. The chances are that you may recognize in yourself or a fellow team member characteristics from one or more "P" type. The important factor here is for managers to determine how people can be motivated to take more responsibility and control for what they do within the team.

1 The Producer

These are people with energy and enthusiasm to get on with the job. They are interested in getting out and getting it done. They are less interested in thinking about what they do or what they ultimately wish to achieve. They know there is much to do and they also know they are good at doing it.

These people are a real bonus to a team, and are likely to require only occasional guidance if they are to achieve the team's objectives. Guidance and encouragement are the main themes of the team manager for producers.

2 The Passenger

Passengers are team members who have slowed their responses to the external demands on the team. They have become preoccupied with process. For them, it is the ride that is important, not the destination. And as the ride has been long and likely to continue, they can settle back to producing an acceptable minimum, undemanding level of outputs.

These people are the team historians and have often lived through the many changes that teams have experienced in the last 10-20 years. They have "seen 'em come and seen 'em go!" The manager will want to provide new challenges for them which disrupt the comfortable routine that has ebbed away their energy. A project, a small evaluation study on which the whole of the team depends could be the way forward here. Direction, encouragement, and monitoring are the manager's themes with the team's passengers.

3 The Prisoner

Prisoners only dream of escaping. They find it difficult to engage actively with the changing face of teamwork, and often reminisce about the days when specialist skills were valued and their status recognized within the team. They become the victims of change, too fearful of what change will bring to engage with it in creative or ameliorative ways. They hide and sometimes stagnate within teams, and too often are not acknowledged as serious contributors.

A move, an new activity is what is called for here. A challenge that safely tests the strengths of the prisoner and invites the assumption of new responsibilities. The manager must be determined not to allow the prisoner to hide or to become a second class contributor to the team effort. A challenge, with support and guidance, along with regular monitoring of achievement is a good remedy for prisoners. Help them break out!

4 The Poseur

We've all seen the poseur. A person of presence, of dignity and charm! Usually intelligent. Often uninformed. But their role within the team, defined either by behaviour or status, in some way carries credibility. It could be that the poseur is powerful because of organisational position, or as a self-selecting or team-selected expert. In either case, playing the expert is more important than having expertise.

Poseurs are potentially dangerous people. Humiliating them in public is unproductive and often leads to unpleasant consequences for all concerned. The supportive challenge may be more effective here. Managers would want to challenge in ways which do not lead to admissions of ignorance and yet encourage poseurs to make more effective use of their intellectual energies. An indirect challenge is useful, such as, "I am interested in what you have just said. Where did you get this information?" Managers will recognise the poseur's insecurities and both challenge and guide sensitively.

5 The Poisoner

Beware the poisoner, the team member who seems to know why everything goes wrong but insists it is for others to put right. Poisoners stop good things happening, and it only takes one per team! They seem to have a real investment in helping things not work so that they can enjoy the chaos that makes them feel better about themselves.

Managers can put much energy into managing poisoners and their effects. They may find more success in trying to shift the poisoner into another "P" type and taking the appropriate action there. Unfortunately, many poisoners have too few tools in their toolbag, and some can do nothing else. For those who can't be diverted from their poisoning ways, there is no alternative to early retirement, redundancy, or termination of employment following disciplinary action. A hard road for all concerned, but one well worth taking. In these extreme cases, there is only one solution: to help the poisoner have a nice day elsewhere!

CHANGE AND RESISTANCE

You already know that community care agencies have not remained static over the past two decades. The rate of change increases as the implications of the NHS and Community Care Act are played out. The separation of the commissioning, purchasing and providing functions, needs-led assessments and individual service planning have all required new perspectives of existing inter-agency relationships. New roles spawning new types of conversations and activities have introduced unfamiliar practices in relating to colleagues. This can be an exciting and innovative time, when creativity and personal resourcefulness achieve better service user-centred care and support. But because change always includes elements of the unfamiliar and a resultant feeling of instability, staff can become over-anxious of the consequences of change. They can become reluctant to engage in the processes which lead to the successful resolution of problems and implementation of change. It is sometimes difficult to remember that care agencies which survived the demanding time of the 1980's did so by continually anticipating, adjusting, changing and reviewing their major activities and relationships.

Change is itself the opportunity for conflict, and you will find it is more productive to manage the conflict openly than down-play the opportunity itself. Conflict, though painful, is an intense lesson whereby the agency learns about itself. Resistance is the by-product of conflict and is by its nature more difficult to manage. Both need to be managed — not controlled — and each requires fundamentally different approaches. Conflict and resistance cannot be controlled; they are more often denied or suppressed. So, if control is not an option, only thoughtful management can bring resolutions.

Conflict is based on disagreement
An idea, a theory, an attitude which is unacceptable to others forms the basis of conflict. It is an expression of the organisational duality that exists in most agencies:

— the them and us
— the impersonal managerial forces raging against professional integrity
— The clashing of ideologies and the people behind them.

Conflict can be either open or covert. Open conflict is easily recognized because it is:

— dramatic
— emotionally draining
— characterised by entrenching into "sides"
— relatively short term
— financially costly.

Because open conflict is so emotionally exhausting to all concerned, it tends to be highly dramatic and relatively short lived.

Covert conflict is demonstrated by a "working to rule" mentality characterised by:

— sluggishness
— emotional denial
— muddling of issues (red herrings)
— longer term disorder
— very high productivity losses

- tendency to create long term damage
- financially very costly – more than open conflict.

Covert conflict is more costly to the agency and its service users because it allows conflict to continue in ways which cannot be openly acknowledged and resolved. The emotional content of the conflict is denied, and the matter of principle (the idea or belief) is emphasized. A siege mentality develops to provide comfort and support to each "side" and to provide a situation in which emotions can be invested. So much energy is invested by each side to keep it's viewpoint intact that there is little left for communication between the sides. This often has to be initiated by an independent facilitator (arbitration).

Resistance is based on dissatisfaction
Feelings of resentment or disappointment can produce behaviours which resemble covert conflict, but their foundation is dissatisfaction rather than disagreement. While resistant behaviour will create rationalisations to explain itself, any resolution is likely to be found at an emotional level rather than in ideology. Seeking agreement helps resolve conflict; seeking satisfaction helps overcome resistance.

Getting the best from colleagues for the benefit of your service user may mean that you will need to be tough, but not cruel. If you enjoy making life difficult for colleagues, the chances are you are being cruel. If you are to be tough you should be confident that you are making demands that will benefit your service user in the longer term and will help the organisation meet its objectives.

Conflict and resistance are understandable reactions to anxiety, so it is important not to be afraid of the anxiety of others. The anxiety of others need not become yours, but you can help them manage their own fears. Help them use their anxiety to bring about the change that needs to happen. It could mean the difference between them being in charge of their own responses and becoming victims of the actions of others.

Anxiety is present in most changing organisations. It is neither your enemy nor your friend, but presents you with an opportunity during times of change. Remember that in the first year following significant change, organisations and the people in them are highly adaptable, provided they have not lurched from one change to another.

Here are five steps for managing conflict and resistance, and for helping others manage their anxiety to best effect:

1 *Be Honest*
   acknowledge uncertainty
   acknowledge potential loss (status, promotions,
       employment)
   acknowledge you may not have the answers
   do not make things appear better than they are

2 *Show Confidence*
   show people that you feel they can get through this time
       of stress
   show people that you trust them to do the right thing

3 *Explore Possibilities*
   be open about the possibilities
   do not advise unless sincerely asked
   spend time with each person to talk about their
       individual circumstances and responses

4 *Show Support*
   show that you understand
   show that personal circumstances are important to you
   ask what support people need and help them arrange it
   leave people in charge of what they do

5 *Communicate Regularly*
   keep people up to date
   make sure they know you understand what they
       are saying
   make sure they can tell you how they hope to respond.

Helping the people who care for vulnerable service users to take responsibility for managing their own professional responses is essential to the perspective that is needed for an empowering community care service. The perspective is that of a team working together to achieve a common goal: the empowerment of service users to maintain or improve the quality of their own lives.

A New Perspective

WORKING AS MEMBERS
OF THE SERVICE USER'S TEAM

HERE is a perspective that reflects a culture change within care agencies. The idea of team working is most often understood in terms of the various professionals participating in a common process or task. However, while most social work teams share a common approach to similar work, it is often hard to detect any significant time when they "work as a team".

Teams are made up of individuals with particular skills and gifts. No two teams are the same because the individual people in them are different. Change one team member and the team becomes something other than it was before. Real teams are not primarily defined in terms of where they are located, but by what they do together. It is the quality of their achievement of the common goal that identifies good teams.

Every team shares a common goal. But there are two fundamentally different kinds of team: single-action and multi-action teams. Single action teams are those where all the team members except the manager perform the same task in roughly the same way to achieve the common goal. Think of a rowing crew! They "pull together", and they are valued as team members because of the similarity of their individual tasks. They achieve the goal by performing almost identical tasks as individuals, creating a momentum which is essentially cumulative.

Multi-action teams demand that each member performs a different task in harmony with the other members to achieve the common goal. Think of a football team. The action is complex, and the team adapts itself to the circumstances as they arise by quickly recognizing which tasks require which skills and assigning them almost instantaneously to the team member with those skills. This team works together. The manager selects team members with specific skills to introduce to the team the benefits that those skills can yield. Each team member has different skills and performs different tasks, but they are co-ordinated and balanced. The team members here are valued because of the diversity of their tasks.

Community care team working requires a multi-action team approach. Health and social care workers form teams which are different from the organisational teams to which they will continue to belong. They form the service user's team! During the time they are all performing diverse tasks for the common benefit of the service user and co-ordinating those tasks with the other professionals involved in the care of the service user, they work AS a team.

THE TEAM SKILL TOOLBOX

**"If all of your tools are hammers,
all of your problems will be nails!"**

Community care teams should function very much like football teams. They should contain the variety of skills required to provide services which empower service users to improve the quality of their own lives. The totality of the team's skills consists of the tools available to each service user for the achievement of this goal.

Imagine that each member of your team carries with them a tool box in which they squeeze all the skills they have developed through training and experience. Each member is likely to have many of the same basic tools as the others, the tools required for the bulk of the work. These are what are known as core skills which most if not all of the team members have. How these core skills are applied in practice will differ because of the individual team member's special interests, personality and enthusiasm.

Each team member's tool box will contain some tools which are not found in the others. These are the special capabilities that each individual team member brings. The special capabilities of all team members should also be available to every service user, because their needs may require special skills that their allocated care manager may not have.

The service user for whom you have responsibility should not be disadvantaged by your personal lack of specialist skills when those skills are "carried" by a member of your team. Unfortunately, case management systems tend to reinforce the tradition of workers involved in their own "caseload" because the line management system extends its hierarchical conventions down through the case allocation processes. Workers are accountable for cases in a hierarchical way and this positively discourages them from investing their specialist skills in the caseloads of colleagues which may desperately need their skilled attention.

Gaining access to the special skills of another team member for the benefit of your service user may present issues for the team's current operating culture and systems. But if these operational problems are resolved, the main difficulty in the team's functioning is resolved. Remember, multi-action teams function on the basis of their differences, not their similarities.

You can plan better use of the team's core and special skills by taking time out as a team to answer these questions:

Given that our goal is to empower service users to improve the quality of their own lives,

1   What are the competencies we need to achieve that goal?

2   What are the competencies available in the team now?

3   How do we gain access to the competencies we do not have?

Where do these competencies exist?

How often do we need to gain access to them?

4   How do we optimise access to the specialist competencies now available within the team?

Identifying skills in this way emphasizes that community care teams are arenas for achieving complex tasks by applying the multiplicity of available skills. This promotes interaction and multi-action team functioning. It also identifies fundamental personal and professional responsibilities to keep up to date with research and theoretical writings.

The quality of outcomes is improved when the diverse roles and skills of the team become more interdependent. The team is at the heart of any quality initiative. Any such initiative depends on authentic working as a team, and the team itself benefits from the powerfully integrating effects of the initiative!

TEAM CULTURE

Working as a member of the service user's team requires no organisational restructuring. There is no need for heavy negotiations about the future of the organisation, and no need to crank up the cumbersome public relations machinery to convince colleagues that one more tampering with the organisation's structure could be the last. However it does require something which much simpler to state yet more difficult to achieve. It requires a shift in the professional's perception about the tasks of community care. It requires a shift in culture!

The required culture shift can be characterised by this statement:

"Instead of the agencies seeing service users as coming into their systems, agencies begin to see themselves as entering the systems of the service user."

Simple? Sounds reasonable? You may feel that your agency already sees its activity as so service user focused that this statement presents no particular challenge. Here is a test to show whether your team or agency is truly service user centred.

THE TEAM CULTURE TEST

The activity of any agency can be evaluated in terms of the information it collects about that activity. Think about your agency and jot down the kinds of data it collects through its information systems. What are the performance indicators, the bits of data that lead managers to a general appreciation of how well or how poorly the agency is performing? Are they quantitative or qualitative?

Quantitative data are essentially about activity and processes, such as:

— number of referrals
— number of allocated cases
— number of unallocated cases
— number of cases over 2 years old
— number of reviews

Qualitative data are about effectiveness and outcomes, such as:

- types of competencies developed or maintained
- improved ability to self manage
- improved ability to develop opportunities for relationships
- improved ability to participate in the care planning process
- improved ability to take responsibility for personal decisions

Now think again about your agency and the printouts that are available to the decision makers and budget holders. What kind of data are they?

If they are quantitative data, it is very likely that your agency views service users in terms of its own processes and organisational requirements. It is collecting information on organisational outputs. Qualitative information may exist in the service user's record, but it is almost irrelevant in terms of agency decision making. It is seldom aggregated into a format which informs the decision making process. The implication here is that the organisation changes to meet the needs of the organisation rather than those of the service user. Decisions are based solely on data with a heavy organisational output bias.

Agencies which allow themselves to enter the service user's system collect primarily qualitative data. While quantitative data will continue to be required for operational planning purposes, the emphasis for service development is to base decision making on the outcomes data they aggregate from the service user records.

A methodology for this is described in THE OUTCOMES, page 73.

The differences between the two types of agency approach are significant and demonstrated graphically on page 76. The agency which collects only quantitative data is primarily concerned with its processes, that is, with what it does, rather than with what it achieves. Qualitative data is essential to the other type of agency because it is driven by its achievements, and adjusts its processes to improve those achievements.

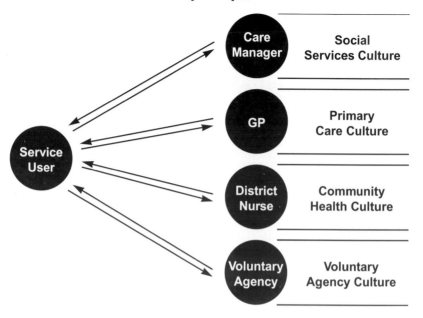

Seeing the service user as entering the agencies' systems

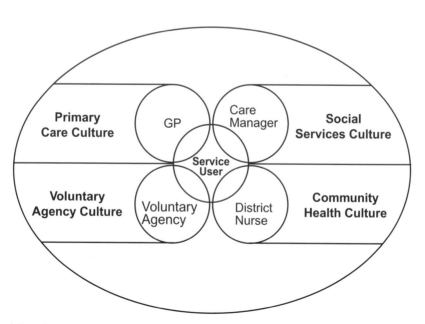

Seeing the agencies as entering the service user's 'system'

The Process

DEVELOPING THE VISION INTO A POLICY

*"A VISION WITHOUT A TASK IS BUT A DREAM A TASK
WITHOUT A VISION IS BUT DRUDGERY A VISION WITH
A TASK! THERE IS THE HOPE OF THE WORLD"*

(Epitaph in Sussex churchyard)

VISION is not a popular word in the 90s. It seems to have combined all the management gloss of the 80s with the messianic appeal of old time religion. The fact is that identifying a vision is hard work, and so it might be convenient to find ways of missing out this vital step. But there is no alternative. Without a vision of what you want to achieve, purpose has no meaning.

A vision for community care is neither divine nor inspired. It is simply an imaginative but realistic insight into the possible quality of life advances for patients and service users which takes into account the service features and linkages that need to be in place to make those advances possible.

Setting the vision establishes the destination. A vision helps you keep on the right track, even though the direction may change when the vision is adjusted from time to time. To have no vision means to have no destination. Without a vision, getting there becomes all the fun! After all, if you don't know where you are going, any road will take you there!

Community care agencies often visualize different destinations or see common destinations differently. It is essential that each agency understands the perspective of the others and negotiates common objectives wherever possible.

The most effective model for developing a common vision is to bring together cross-sections of staff representing all the agencies concerned with community care: Social Services, Housing, Health Commissioners, GPs, community and acute trusts, service user representatives and voluntary agencies. The cross section represents managerial and practitioner levels within each agency. Employing a technique such as brainstorming or mind-mapping, a facilitator (usually independent) takes each group through a series of questions which would look something like this:

What should the service look like?(in three years or so)
What will the major themes be?
What will the major functions be?
What will the roles of the service users and carers be?
What will the professional objectives be?
What will the key organisational concerns be?

What should the service do?
What will the key functions be?
How will these functions relate?

What should the service achieve?
What are the five most important achievements?
How will these achievements be evaluated?
What should the purpose of the service be?
What are the values to be demonstrated in service provision?

How will people work and relate?
How will the service be structured, given its purpose?
How will the professionals network?

A vision statement will contain a broad synthesis of the answers to these questions. It will not be detailed, as that is a matter for a developed strategy and the planning process.

Once the vision statement has been agreed, you have all the material required for establishing a shared policy. There is a simple formula for policy development, and if any one element is missing the policy remains incomplete and, at best, short-term:

VISION + PURPOSE + VALUES = POLICY

Policy is the operational foundation of community care, yet so many agencies continue their work without clearly defined shared policies. For many agencies, policies are developed in response to operational problems rather that as a foundation for operational success. Policy is a comprehensive statement of operational values (the rules of engagement) to be employed and objectives to be achieved in the realisation of PURPOSE.

A great deal of what is contained in current community care plans is really community care policy. The policy tells staff and service users what the agency wants to achieve and why it wants to achieve it. It need not be a detailed document, but a broad clarification of intentions. Details are left to the strategy.

STRATEGY AND THE PLANNING PROCESS

Strategy should follow policy but, sadly, often does not. For some organisations – those which concentrate on their processes at the expense of their achievements – strategy means policy. Strategy without policy is directionless; policy without strategy is sterile.

Whilst policy identifies future achievements and why they are important, strategy identifies how and when those achievements will become reality. Think of strategy as a map and a timetable applying the rules of engagement (the values) to the task (the achievement). It is a plan which sets objectives against timescales which have been agreed as providing the most effective and efficient itinerary for achieving the PURPOSE. Through the strategy and the planning process the vision becomes reality. Without strategy, nothing changes by design, only by default!

Setting the strategy – the plan – is very much like spreading a map out on the table. The starting point is clear, and the destination is clear. The steps and stops along the way may have been identified, but there is no information about the best mode of transport, the weather, or how other considerations can impede progress. Having a strategy is an essential step, but is not good enough on its own without the planning process.

Strategies are bigger than plans just as wars are bigger than battles. They often require different skills and experiences, so the people designing the strategy may not be the right people to take it forward in the planning processes which necessarily follow. Good strategists often make poor planners.

The planning process incorporates the preparatory thinking that applies strategy to practical realities. Here is the decision making that leads to goal setting and change. Good planning never loses sight of the strategy and therefore the purpose, but identifies the areas where operational decisions are required. Good planning achieves clarity and diminishes uncertainty for the staff. It inspires motivation and limits the possibility of failure.

If the strategy is the map and the itinerary, think of planning as the process of packing the bags. It is the thinking ahead to what may be required for applying the strategy to practical realities. Both strategy and the planning process are components of making something better happen by design!

Planning what you do for the people you care for is a mark of your concern to get things right for them. Whether it is a simple or a complex task, planning assists you in helping others understand the services you are providing so that they can derive the most benefit from them.

Planning has a central place in the provision of care services, so it is best to understand what makes good planning. Here are some conditions for good planning:

— Knowledge of the organisational purpose, values and policies
— Knowledge of the organisational strategy
— Good problem identification and analysis skills
— Ease in consulting people who know about key issues
— Good decision making experience
— Sound implementation experience
— Evaluation skills

Planning Objectives
The objectives of planning are usually characterised in three ways: maintenance, innovation, and speculation.

1   Maintenance Planning
    This is the planning process which seeks to continue current activity with fewer resources. It will concentrate on reducing "overheads"; in other words, activity which is not directly related to service provision will be revised. Emphasis here will be on maintaining the activity and modifying its relationships with other processes.

2   Innovative Planning
    This is planning to increase the current activity with fewer resources. Here is the testing of alternative service provision possibilities. Innovative planning requires the acceptance and management of higher levels of risk to the organisation, and perhaps even to its service users.

3   Speculative Planning
    This planning moves beyond current activity and con-
    jectures about future possibilities. It sets out a
    programme of experimentation with alternatives within
    an agreed vision of what that future might look like, in
    terms of service user need and the inter-relatedness of
    future community care services.

Planning Models

Systems of planning reflect the organisation's communication and decision making culture. The processes of
planning are likely to mirror other processes within the
organisation, so studying one gives you the opportunity to
comment on the other!

There are five fundamental models for planning in organisations:

1 Top-Down Planning

All data for planning are processed and interpreted within
the higher management levels of the agency. The emphasis here is on the strategic approach, which often decrees
the direction of service development in accordance with the
managerial interpretation of the vision. This is done without
reference to the current capability of the organisation. If
such consultation exists, it is usually brief and (literally) a
paper exercise. Change becomes the agenda, and a limited VISION drives that change toward what are likely to be
short term benefits!

2 Bottom-Up Planning

All the information required for planning is available to and
interpreted by the staff who are closest to the point of service delivery. This model usefully reflects the organisation's
current experience, its capability to deliver services. But is
this an improvement, given the possibly limited appreciation of the overall strategic objectives of the service? Too
often this model leads to no change and creates an arena
where the needs of staff compete directly with the needs of
service users. EXPERIENCE stagnates, providing rationalisations for its unwillingness to change!

3 Conflictive Planning

These plans arise when one part of the organisation does not communicate effectively with another, or where agencies do not work closely enough with each other. Here vision is detached from experience. Agencies, caught up in the drama of their own processes, fail to recognize the roles of the others in providing services to the service users they have in common. Multiple VISIONS ignore the varied EXPERIENCE of the agencies.

4 Biased Planning

This process represents a move in the right direction, but it is still not good enough. Planning in this way often shows a dominance of the vision over the experience of the organisation, and often leads to higher discontent. Unbalanced planning is characterized by consultation for appearances rather than for real debate, a universally dissatisfying process. Often the higher status of managers helps them ensure that VISION overpowers EXPERIENCE!

5 Balanced Planning

This is the one to aim for! It is not just a matter of getting the views of the workers and service users in front of the managers. It is about achieving the balance of those views within an informed understanding of the agency's stated purpose and values. This represents the balancing of VISION and EXPERIENCE, and is the gateway to more effective organisational performance. That can only be good news for the service user.

PLANNING IN A POLITICAL CULTURE

Planning in most organisations takes place within a political culture. Community care agencies are not an exception to this general rule, so it is important to be politically aware (both with a small p and with a big P). Planning within a political culture requires preparation and analysis which addresses your answers to these four groups of considerations:

1 **WHAT** activity (exactly) is being planned?
   What are the major themes of the activity?
   What are the outcomes being sought? What are the likely benefits?

What problems could arise? (see Forecasting and Analysis below)
What information is required?
What protocols need to be in place?
What support is needed and from whom?
What criteria will be used for measuring success?

2   **WHO** is to be involved?
Who benefits and how?
Who is disadvantaged and how?
Who is involved and in what roles?
Who needs to be kept informed?

3   **HOW** will the activity affect current systems and relationships?
How will the people involved communicate?
How will multi-agency decisions be taken?
How will the required information be shared?
How will the training integrate with each agency's requirements?
How will the information systems provide data for the evaluation of the activity?

4   **WHEN** will the new activity take place?
When must the outcomes of the activity be in place?
When must each objective of the activity be achieved and in what order?
When must the activity be started?
When must data collection for the evaluation be started?
When are the interim and final evaluation reports due?

There is no adequate substitute for good operational planning. Policy documents and the strategy which reflects policy are the foundation of good planning, but are not the whole of the planning process. Consistent attention to priorities and contingencies requires steady planning effort if implementation problems are to be minimized.

Problem Forecasting and Analysis

Let's get this straight from the start: Problems are not opportunities! The two concepts are fundamentally different and identifying one with the other only serves to confuse the planning activity. Telling colleagues that problems are really opportunities waiting to happen firmly marks you as a Poseur (see page 46). Problems reflect situations or conditions which need resolution or curative treatment. Opportunities potentially bring benefits. To seize the opportunity without solving the underlying problem only stores up longer term grief, particularly when the conditions identified in the problem remain. Taking opportunities does not solve problems, and it is difficult for opportunities to yield their benefits on the seedbed of unresolved problems.

Forecasting what problems might arise as a result of a proposed activity is crucial. Some people will not see a problem coming straight towards them. Others plan for every problematic possibility. As a good planner you will not waste time identifying and analysing problems which have a low probability of occurring. There should be a balance where potential problems are identified and rated against a scale such as this:

Certainty	when the planned action will leave no alternative to a problem or problem chain occurring quickly
High Probability	when the planned action is very likely to raise a problem in the very near future
Probability	when the planned action could easily raise a problem in the near or medium term future
Low Probability	when the planned action may raise a problem in the near or medium future
Lowest Probability	when the planned action is unlikely to raise a problem in the near or medium future

Problems, of course, come in all shapes and sizes, and good problem forecasting and analysis techniques demand that planners assess the potential damage the problem could inflict, either on the implementation stages of service planning (short term damage) or on the services themselves (long term damage). Problems could be assessed against these criteria:

Critical	problems arising from fundamental conflicts of interest or perception which are likely to bring implementation to a standstill
Serious	problems arising from organisational conflicts of policy or accountabilities which are likely to delay implementation
Significant	problems arising from operational conflicts of procedure or method which are likely to delay implementation
Symptomatic	problems arising from conflicts associated with the implementation process itself (resistance, grievances, etc)
Minor	problems arising from conflicts identified day by day through the implementation phase

Screening each problem against these criteria helps you determine which problems are priorities for further analysis. It may be that resources and time allow only critical or serious problems you assess to be a certainty or highly probable to receive further analysis. With the grid on page 66, you can easily screen problems and make decisions about which levels of probability or severity require no further analysis at this time.

Probability → Significance →	Certainty	High Probability	Probability	Low Probability	Lowest Probability
Critical					
Serious					
Significant					
Symptomatic					
Minor					

Method of Problem Analysis
The problem with problems is that though they may disappear with proper management, their effects can remain. Solving the problem is not enough. For long lasting resolutions the cause of the problem must be eliminated. Any proposed solution addressing only the problem is likely to produce effects which are themselves causes of other problems. These in their turn will require future attention. The "quick and dirty" solution to problems could well litter the agency with difficulties and dilemmas requiring progressively more management time and skill to resolve.

There are many techniques for developing better understanding of problems. The SWOT method is very popular with many managers and management training specialists, and has its place in problem analysis. SWOT analysis stands for:

Strengths
Weaknesses
Opportunities
Threats

There is an argument that SWOT analyses don't go far enough. They tend to be analyses of proposed action rather than of the problem or circumstances calling for that action. Full problem analysis addresses three distinct aspects of a given situation or condition:

1 the problem
2 the proposed action
3 the predicted outcome

Stage One – understanding the problem
This means seeing the problem in context, not in isolation. A better understanding of the linkages and the aspects of the problem is more likely to lead to a better action plan. Here, the PEST analysis takes the lead. PEST stands for:

Political
Economic
Social
Technical

What are the PEST implications of the problem? What are the PEST ramifications? Is the problem politically generated or can it be politically tolerated? Is the problem economically supportable or unacceptable? What are the implications for the service user and the staff if the problem remains unresolved? What are the implications for information systems and the logistics of service delivery if the problem continues unaddressed?

Good planning makes sure that the problem is understood, and a PEST analysis helps that understanding by placing the problem in context. In the real world, there are no free-standing problems. They all link to somewhere else.

Stage Two – proposing the right action
SWOT analyses mainly look at proposed actions, not problems. Remember:

Strengths
Weaknesses
Opportunities
Threats

What are the strengths and weaknesses of our proposed action? What new opportunities is it likely to bring? What could impede its progress? How will it adversely affect other agency activities?

Planning is about action, so SWOT analyses play a central part in identifying the right action in the circumstances. Linking SWOT and PEST analyses promotes a stronger understanding of those circumstances.

Stage Three – looking for the right outcomes
This is essentially the predictive element in the problem analysis process. Here planners anticipate what the outcomes of the proposed action will be and then ask these four questions. This is the ECHO analysis, and this stands for:

Effect (Outcomes)
Consequences
Harm
Outputs

What are the outcomes that can be predicted to occur should this proposed action take place concerning this given problem? In other words, what are the predictive outcomes of our action? What consequences will those outcomes spill onto the organisation, it staff and its service users? Who could be harmed by this action and how? What would be placed at risk? And finally, what are the new or additional outputs required to ensure that the action yields the outcomes we are looking for?

Problem identification and analysis is essential to the planning process. All problems have a context which has to be understood before appropriate corrective action can be identified. That corrective action will have intended and sometimes unintended outcomes, and anticipating those possibilities tempers and informs the "fix" mentality that can sometimes dominate managerial solutions to service implementation problems.

MAKING SOMETHING GOOD HAPPEN

The planning is done and review mechanisms put in place. The decisions have been made and the proposed action has been clearly identified. The quality initiative has been blessed and launched. What now? How can you make sure something of quality happens?

Think of quality as the flowers in a garden. If the garden is well kept and surrounded by well maintained shrubs, and the flower beds are fed and watered with care, then the beauty of the flowers will be recognized against the background of the garden. The sight of an excellent rose managing to grow amongst the decaying cabbages is both rare and incongruous. Excellent as the rose may be, few benefit from seeing its perfection. To most observers the rose is sadly out of place.

Quality, like the rose, needs a context, a climate in which to grow and become part of a wider culture. The achievement of quality is a matter for the whole of the organisation, not just the quality assurance manager. Having such a post does not absolve the rest of the organisation from its responsibilities for working toward quality outcomes.

Negative influences exist in most agencies, making the establishment of a quality climate all the more critical. There are eight common organisational characteristics which indicate that a new climate for producing outputs of quality is needed:

1   Unclear expectations between managerial and professional levels

2   Vague or undefined or unnegotiated responsibilities

3   A feeling of lack of control and inability to influence decision making

4   Staff shortages and skill deficits

5   Poor and unfocused training

6   Poor physical surroundings for staff and service users

7   Unrealistic pace of change
Changing work practices without consultation

Too many changes simultaneously involving the same people

8   Changing systems when they are already effective

Establishing a quality climate has the effect of unlocking skills and imagination. Quality orientated agencies look toward their achievements first and their processes second. They are characterised by:

Enthusiasm   The energy of commitment. It attracts confidence and generates further energy

Imagination   The ability to visualise possibilities and suggest alternatives. This is also the force behind effective lateral thinking

Maximisation   The lowering of artificial boundaries that impede progress. This means introducing financial and organisational flexibility

Consultation   The sharing of information and responsibilities. This means the agency is collaborating with its own staff and other agencies

Pride   The self-esteem that comes from playing a part in an agency determined to help people improve the quality of their own lives. People can point to their contribution to the processes and the outcomes.

How can a quality climate be established and maintained? Here is an eight stage programme for those wishing to cultivate quality outcomes within community care organisations.

Stage One: Become very clear about what is meant by "quality"(see page 70). Remember, it means different things to each person, so it is important that your agency (or team) agree on how you are using the word and understanding the concept behind the word.

Stage Two: Learn what your managers expect of you. Ask them to specify exactly what they are looking for in terms of outcomes from your part of the agency. Negotiate a better way of working within those expectations where you can, and try to outline the benefits for them should your pursuit of quality outcomes be successful.

Stage Three: Identify the problems that could inhibit the development of quality services, and assess their potential impact (see Problem Forecasting and Analysis on page 63).

What are the personal agendas and what are the content and sources of any hidden agendas?

What is the level of trust in the organisation, and does it require remedial action to raise it to a level that more easily accommodates change?

Who are the strategic thinkers and how can they be enlisted into the programme for improving quality?

How does the agency communicate within itself and with other organisations? Are communications effective and, if not, why not?

Stage Four: Develop your plan for making service outcomes more effective and the work of the agency more effective in achieving its purpose. Listen and talk with colleagues about how they see the work of the agency responding to current and future need. Help them put their ideas into practice, always trying to say "yes" and "why not?" to good ideas. Helping people build confidence in their own ideas generates the energy to bring their ideas closer to reality.

Stage Five: Publicise the plan so that the agency and service users know what you want to achieve. Senior management commitment is necessary, but don't stop there. Consult colleagues within your agency and in partner organisations about what you hope to achieve and be seen to consult them. Manage any resistance with openness and honesty (see CHANGE AND RESISTANCE TO CHANGE on page 47) and acknowledge past failures without in any way taking responsibility for failures which are not yours. Openly accept failures which are yours and do not blame other people or systems.

Stage Six: Implement the new service or development and make your expectations clear about its anticipated benefits by identifying specific outcomes you hope to achieve. Develop performance indicators that show qualitative trends as well as quantitative and which address both processes and outcomes.

Stage Seven: Ensure that your energy and that of your implementation team is maintained. Seek good supervision in whatever form is most useful to you and arrange for critical input regarding the progress of the quality initiative to be a regular feature of your monitoring activities.

Stage Eight: Review what you are doing and evaluate it in terms of the overall purpose and values of the organisation. It is helpful to engage an independent source of evaluation so that objectivity is maintained.

Establishing the quality culture in an organisation requires sustained energy, particularly in the early stages. Once the benefits of the initiatives born of that culture begin to be recognized, this energy can be extended to new ventures that improve community care services.

The Outcome

**"Its not what you do that really counts:
it's what you achieve!"**

OUTCOMES are what we achieve; outputs are what
we do to achieve outcomes. Outcomes are much
talked about as reality, and indeed they are the
real results of agency interventions. However, they often go
unrecognized and uncounted. Instead outputs have
become the subject of much accounting attention. As we
have seen, organisations that spend too much of their
resources collecting data relating to their activity come to
see that activity as their purpose, and not merely the
means of achieving their purpose. Quantitative data
churned out regularly on oceans of printouts only confirm
the agency's obsession with activity. This is usually
achieved at the cost of not auditing real outcomes. For
these agencies it seems safer to feel busy than to make
the time for what is seen to be a lesser priority or even a
fringe activity: ensuring effectiveness. They may be fearful
that identified outcomes would bear no relation to the outcomes they intended to achieve. Surely this would be
failure, so why put the energy into serving up bad news?

Well, it is likely to serve up good news, too. Because
the people to whom we provide services are often the most
vulnerable in the community, travelling in hope without
good qualitative information about agency effectiveness is
no longer professionally acceptable.

Everything depends on purpose, as we have seen in
the earlier chapters of this book. Measuring outcomes is
effectively measuring the agency's success or failure in
achieving the outcomes it predicted it would achieve.
Purpose can be defined in terms of output or in terms of
outcomes. It is important to understand that these are two
significantly different ways of defining purpose, with sub-
stantially different implications for how they measure
success. Look at two definitions from two fictitious community care providers.

Agency Alpha
**The purpose of this organisation is to provide commu-
nity care housing, employment opportunities and day**

care services to people with disabilities living in the community.

This purpose statement clearly sets out what the agency does, and that is helpful in itself. What kind of data will be collected so that the agency can evaluate how well it is doing what it does? It will probably collect:

— service user population numbers
— numbers of allocated cases
— numbers of cases on waiting lists
— numbers of assessments
— numbers of service reviews
— expenditure per service user contact

It will collect this quantitative data because that is completely in keeping with its purpose! Its success is measured in terms of its activities: service user contacts, processes and service provision. The agency judges its success solely in terms of what it does. It is essentially inward looking.

INWARD LOOKING AGENCY – CHARACTERISTICS

Records and monitors activity
Identifies and controls unit costs
Amends activity to become more "efficient"

Agency Beta
The purpose of this organisation is to empower disadvantaged and devalued people to improve the quality of their own lives.

This purpose statement clearly sets out a broad declaration of what the agency intends to achieve. The kind of information this agency collects about its achievements will mean it asking itself:

— what capabilities have service users developed?
— how have those capabilities been demonstrated?
— how have those capabilities been generalized to other situations facing the service user?
— what enhancements are evident in service users' self-esteem?
— which institutionalized behaviours have diminished?
— what opportunities have service users developed for personal relationships?

- increased participation in their service planning?
- new occupation/employment experiences?
- enhancing their responsibilities toward the community?
- representing the views of others?

These data are essentially qualitative. Here is an agency that is primarily concerned with achieving outcomes which empower. How they do it — that is, what the agency does to achieve this purpose — is important only in so far as what it does is effective in achieving empowering outcomes. This agency measures its success in terms of what it achieves! It is both outward and inward looking.

OUTWARD AND INWARD LOOKING AGENCY – CHARACTERISTICS

OUTWARD LOOKING	INWARD LOOKING
Predicts outcomes	Determines activities
Reviews outcomes	Relates processes to achievements
Measures achievement of predicted social outcomes	Amends activities to become more effective

MEASURING SOCIAL OUTCOMES

It is not difficult to measure social outcomes, but it is different! It is not difficult inasmuch as the data source already exists for all the outcome measuring an agency needs to do. That data source is the service user's record.

Here is a good question: Why does your agency not aggregate outcome information from service user files in the same way it collects intervention (activity) information? Think about it! Confidentiality cannot be the pretext for not developing a database for outcomes because it is the outcome and not the service user's personal information that is relevant. The answer is likely to be that this kind of data collection does not fit the operating culture of the organisation (see page 23). Remember, if activity is the agency purpose, outcome (achievement) measurement becomes both a threatening and a peripheral activity.

In reality, measuring outcomes can be as easy as measuring outputs once the agency decides that it is important enough to be done! That is the genuine problem – the real stumbling block! The data sources – the service users' records – is available and contains valuable outcome information which is generally not otherwise accessible. Sometimes the agency's eagerness to close files and start new activities (because they are contracted for the activities and not the achievements) denies them access to their most important information for planning.

Measuring outcomes is easy, but it is different from what you are probably doing now. There is a method that takes a short time to set up within an agency, but once in place generates minimal additional work. The method has three stages:

1 IDENTIFYING Predictive Outcomes

2 APPLYING Quantitative Techniques to Qualitative Data

3 MONITORING Predictive Outcomes

Stage One Identifying Predictive Outcomes
Predictive outcomes are those the empowering agencies hope to achieve with and for their service user. Think for a moment about what you hope your health and social care interventions will achieve for your service users as individuals. What sort of capabilities would you be working for them to maintain and develop so that they could maintain or improve the quality of their lives?

It is essential that each agency determines for itself what it intends to achieve for its service users. It is just as important that they involve those service users in that process. Outcomes will be different for every agency and they should be. They should be fully in keeping with the agency's defined purpose and values. Once established they should not become the agency's monolithic statement of good intentions for all time. They will change because the needs of the service users will change. They must be regularly reviewed, and the annual business planning cycle provides a useful event for such a review.

Here is an example of predictive outcomes for you to consider. Remember how important it is for each agency to develop their own list of outcomes. It needs to be in the agency's own words for those words to have the force they need to make outcome measurement happen. People are more enthusiastic about their own ideas and words rather than ideas and words from others, so exploit the creative thinking within your own agency.

Predictive Outcomes in Community Care

1   Maintained or increased self achievement
    Types of competencies developed
    Number of competencies developed
    Increase in the number of situations where competencies are demonstrated
    Resultant increase in self-esteem

2   Diminished dependency which is not associated with disability (diminished institutionalized behaviour)
    Types of dependency behaviours diminished
    Number of dependency behaviours diminished
    Increase in ability to respond authentically and personally to institutionalizing carers and care systems

3   Increased social participation
    Increased opportunities for personal relationships
    Increased participation in the care planning process
    Improvement in the quality of negotiation
    Increase in persistence in communicating personal opinion
    Development of personal influence skills

4   Increased expectations
    Shift from acceptance of services to asking why
    Shift in the planning focus from care to interdependence
    Shift from accepting the minimum acceptable to insisting on what is good enough
    Increase in the concern to clarify roles (who is responsible for what)

5   How service users empower others
    Enhanced sense of responsibility toward their community
    Decreased self-centred, reactive responses
    Increased opportunities to represent the views of others
    Increased intention to collaborate rather than simply be consulted

Stage Two Applying Quantitative Techniques to Qualitative Data

Now that the predictive outcomes have been identified, it is simply a matter of assigning a code to each outcome you wish to monitor. This is so that the data can be collected on any standard spreadsheet software. It can of course be collected manually, but collating the data and interrogating it would be hugely labour intensive in that format. It is much better to assign codes to each outcome and then simply arrange your systems to collect data in the coded form.

Here is a suggested way of coding using the example of predictive outcomes above. The actual competency may be the ability to pay rent. Your code could look something like this:

1   Maintained or increased self achievement
5   ability to pay rent

The code would then be "1.5".

Another sample code from the third example. Say you wish to measure how successful your agency is in helping its service users develop opportunities for relationships. Remember, here you are not measuring the quality of those relationships, even though this is familiar territory for social workers. Here you are measuring your service user's ability to obtain for themselves the opportunities required for developing personal relationships. The ability to visit local social clubs could be an intended outcome which, amongst other possible outcomes, indicates a level of social participation. Attending social clubs might be placed fourth on your list of outcomes. In this case your code could look like this:

3   Increased social participation
4   ability to visit the local social club

The code for this outcome is then "3.4".

If, by chance, attending social clubs was placed sixth on your list of outcomes indicating social participation, your code would then be "3.6".

You may need to take advice as to how to code your outcomes given the spreadsheet programme at your disposal. Once you have the outcomes coded, the spreadsheet you design will simply collect data relating to the codes.

Stage Three Monitoring Predictive Outcomes
There will be two occasions when you will wish to input data into the spreadsheet: firstly, when services are being designed following assessment; and secondly, when those

services are being reviewed (see the example of a simple spreadsheet below).

Service User's Name:								
1 Outcome	2 Achievement Targets					3 Achievement		4 Reason for Non-Achievement or Partial Achievement
	Time Target Months			Before Target	Y	N	P	
Code	3	6	9	12				

When services are being designed and agreed, the codes for the outcomes you wish to achieve before the first review are input onto the spreadsheet. There is also a space to indicate when you have agreed with the service user that this outcome should occur. In the example, there are boxes for three months or six months. You do not return to the spreadsheet until the first service review is completed. Only then are you able to complete the spreadsheet and establish further predictive outcome information for the next review.

Following the first service review, return to the spreadsheet and complete it. In the case of this example, you will need to:
— identify whether the outcome was achieved within the intended time
— if not, why not
— if partially achieved, why? if the activity leading to the outcome was not completed for any reason, why?

All the possible reasons for non or partial achievement are also coded. They could include the following:
— staff shortages
— skill deficits
— too ambitious target setting
— inappropriate target setting
— financial shortages
— resource unavailability
— physical health deterioration of the service user
— task beyond the capability of the main carer.

Individual service user monitoring spreadsheets feed into a larger electronically held team-based or agency-based spreadsheet. The result is that the individual spreadsheet stays with the service user's record as a personal record, while the coded data is aggregated up to the agency spreadsheet. This means that the agency is beginning to collect information on how effective it is becoming at empowering people to develop skills for improving the quality of their own lives.

You may well need specialist advice regarding the setting up of the spreadsheet system. Find the arrangement that best suits your agency and your team. You may wish to practice with two or three outcomes to begin with until confidence is high enough in the team to take on more. It will probably take a year or, say, about 200 outcome measurements to build up sufficient data to influence how the agency plans its service activities. By that time, you should be forming a good understanding of what the agency is good at achieving and what it is not. You will know more about how long it takes you to achieve complex outcomes, and the reasons for your failing to achieve some outcomes on time.

The Potential Benefits of Measuring Social Outcomes

The benefits that accrue when the agency measures its effectiveness in empowering people to improve the quality of their own lives are ultimately to the service user. All of the predictive outcomes in the example above relate directly or indirectly to quality of life issues. It is the capabilities of the service user that are being developed by the intervention of the organisation. To do that effectively, the agency itself has to become capable of ensuring that its interventions are empowering.

There are two significant benefits to an organisation which measures its outcomes. Particularly in the field of health and social care, where multiple processes abound and interact, it is essential that these most personal of services are effective. The first benefit is that in measuring social outcomes the agency necessarily looks outside itself to the needs of its service users. At a time when community care plans and patients' charters are the currency for promoting the personal nature of health and social care, measuring social outcomes becomes essential.

The second benefit has potentially far reaching implications for the commissioning process. Measuring outcomes begins to change the language of the contracts which embody the commissioning process. Most commissioning agencies develop contracts relating to the activities of provider trusts and agencies. They contract for events, episodes, and service user "contacts". This is a particularly irrelevant way of commissioning community care services. Much provider energy goes into feeding quantitative data collection systems with contact numbers while little or no data is collected relating to the effectiveness of these contacts. Commissioners are learning how to ask questions about quality that require more than quantitative answers, and providers are learning that they have first to develop methods of demonstrating effectiveness as well as efficiency. Remember, efficiency means nothing if it is not related to effectiveness. Commissioners will be asking questions about the quality of services through their contracting process (service specifications and standards) and providers will need to develop the ability to respond in qualitative terms.

Empowerment is the business of community care, and the services which empower are those where quality exists. Measuring social outcomes provides a powerful understanding of how to determine the quality of health and social care services. In community care, the measurement of empowerment is the measurement of quality.

The Evaluation

"IT HELPS TO KNOW WHAT YOU ARE DOING!"

IT does help to know what you are doing. It does not always help to know what you did. Long term research programmes have the sometimes unhelpful effect of telling you where you went wrong months ago. It would be more helpful to have known then so that adjustments could have been made to make your services more effective or efficient. What is needed is a way of researching both the processes and the outcomes of your services that runs simultaneously with the provision of those services and the achievement of those outcomes. A useful approach is action research. This is not "pure" research in the traditional sense, but it is often the most effective form of evaluation for agencies where service delivery is both complex and relentless.

Action research is the systematic study of an identified situation or service for the purpose of facilitating change. The research itself helps necessary change to happen. Here there is no detached, analytical view which records activity simply for the purpose of recommending changes. Instead, research and development proceed hand-in-hand, each sustaining the other.

The action researcher is an active participant in the change process. In action research the researcher's role in the change process has six aspects: the researcher

- identifies the need for change
- facilitates change
- becomes a catalyst for change
- becomes an agent for change – becomes a communicator for change – evaluates the progress of change

These roles can, of course, be taken up by other members of the team. The point here is that action researchers are not detached observers. They participate. They record, analyze and interpret data with a view to feeding it back to the team or agency at timely intervals so that the change process (the quality initiative, if you like) benefits more immediately from the evaluation process.

The main characteristics of the action research approach are:

- evaluative as well as descriptive
- qualitative as well as quantitative
- subjective as well as objective
- small in scale but "totality" focused
- responsive to specific needs as they arise
- responsive to unpredicted events as they arise
- dynamic
- complex.

Action research offers agencies the opportunity to learn as they go with new service delivery objectives and systems. This model will be most successful in agencies which:

- are open to new learning
- are communicative
- value continuous monitoring and feedback
- see mistakes as part of the learning process
- work in partnerships with service users and other agencies
- are prepared to apply research findings to their operations for the benefit of the population they serve.

The success of action research depends on good working relationships between the researcher and the agency reviewing its service provision. The researcher brings specialist knowledge, skills and experience to work alongside the people who are providing community care services. Responsibility for ensuring that the research is carried out rests with the agency, but the effectiveness of the research relies also on positive working relationships between the researcher and the other agencies working in partnership with the agency where the research is taking place.

Researchers in local government and other public sector agencies are increasingly adopting an action research approach to service development and organisational change, yet references to action research in the academic literature are rare. The reticence on the part of researchers to catalogue their work in this area can probably be attributed to fear of being judged as insufficiently rigorous. In fact, action research does not compromise academic rigour. Concerns about basic criteria such as validity and reliability remain central. Scrupulous recording of the sequence of events is essential to producing the analyses from which decisions can be made. Action research provides the opportunity for answering key questions in a timely manner and for responding to new questions as they arise in the change process. Like all research methods, it cannot answer questions which are not asked or for which no data source exists to provide the answers.

Action research observes the rigour of academic research. It must answer the basic questions about the research process which are common to all types of research projects:

— What is the shape of the study?
— What methods of data collection are the most appropriate?
— Who will do the work?
    collect data
    provide analysis
    supervise
    produce interim and final reports
— What specialist help will be needed?
— How long will it take? What are the stages and timescales?
— How does it link with other activities within the agency?
— To whom should the results be communicated and how?

ASKING ALL THE RIGHT QUESTIONS

This is where many research or evaluation projects go wrong. They go wrong from the start! How often have agency staff looked to research to provide answers to questions that either have not been asked or cannot be answered! It is often difficult for them to understand why it is important to be very clear about what they want to know about their activity. It is even more difficult for everyone involved in the services, and therefore in the evaluation, to have an overview of just what sort of questions are being asked. Very few people, if any, are able to understand the totality of the evaluation process during the evaluation period. This is partly because they are probably more comfortable with the doing of community care than with the reflection required by evaluation studies. Often enough, they do not have the tools to ensure that a holistic approach is taken.

A system for analysing the suitability of questions exists, however, and it has the important advantage of being able to demonstrate the types of questions that are being asked before valuable resources are put into the evaluation process. This is not a model of research, such as the action research model described earlier. This is a systematic and easily used tool which, if handled correctly and consistently, provides a visual image of how the final report is likely to be balanced. It provides this useful image before data are collected and analyzed, in good time to adjust the focus of the questions to give a more balanced effect.

This system simply involves using something called the Evaluation Grid. It has been adapted to the special research requirements for measuring quality in community care initiatives.

Evaluation studies may include outcome measurement but are not limited to looking at outcomes. Evaluation studies look to collecting information which is broader than outcomes. The Evaluation Grid is a mechanism for framing evaluation questions into a comprehensible structure. It has been developed on the understanding that quality is not simply a matter of outcomes, but a matter of processes and structures (see Donabedian, page 103). The services of any community care team are characterized by specific structures, a variety of processes and a number of predictive outcomes both for the service user and the organisation itself. All three aspects – structures, processes and outcomes – are rightly the subject of research because **the quality of work produced by the team is a result of the interaction of all three aspects.**

The Evaluation Grid provides a method for all those commissioning the research to be assured very early in the process that:

– the questions they have asked relate to all the aspects of the service they wish to investigate

– the questions they have asked are the questions for which they want answers

– the questions they have asked can be answered.

When these questions are satisfactorily answered the agency is more able to give a commitment to the results of the evaluation study.

Outcomes are of two types: user outcomes and organisational outcomes. In addition, there are four aspects of community care services which need to be addressed by evaluation:

— Structures: how the services are designed and set up
— Processes: what activities are associated with the services
— Outcomes (organisational): the effects of the services for the organisation itself
— Outcomes (service user): the effects of the services for those using the services

The Evaluation Grid contains twenty boxes, set out in five columns down and four rows across. The column of four boxes at the extreme left contain statements relating to these aspects of evaluation (see page 89). These statements are simply examples which help interpret the kinds of activities or conditions appropriate to each of the four aspects. The following list may be more helpful because it is more complete:

STRUCTURE
— legal requirements
— published service statements
— charters
— service eligibility criteria
— physical amenities
    location
    accessibility
    suitability of facilities
— personnel
    numbers
    grades, qualifications

PROCESS
— screening
— assessment
— planning
— communication
    internal
    external
— co-ordination
— service user participation
— systems for developing user choice
— information systems
    establishment
    maintenance

OUTCOMES (ORGANISATION)
- training
- supervision
- budget management
- access to information

OUTCOMES (SERVICE USER)
- relationship of outcome to assessment
- relationship of outcome to intervention
- complaints
- problem solving
- advocacy
- degree of user
    understanding
    participation
    satisfaction

The rows across the top of the grid (from the second to the fifth column) should be labelled representing the particular feature of the community care initiative to be evaluated. In theory you could extend the number of these boxes to the right to capture data on a larger number of features you may wish to evaluate. The example here identifies four areas of common concern that may be a good place to start. The service features which are likely to be of high interest to service commissioners, providers and service users themselves are:

Access – to the services of the team
Professional management – of those services
Interpersonal processes – a vital factor in personal services
Continuity – how the services themselves link and relate
           – how the services integrate with other events in the service user's life.

	ACCESS	PROFESSIONAL MANAGEMENT	INTERPERSONAL PROCESSES	CONTINUITY
STRUCTURE Legal requirements Service Statement Physical amenities location accesibility Personal numbers qualifications % Eligibility Criteria				
PROCESS Assessment Planning Communication Co-ordination User participation Info maintenance				
OUTCOMES (ORGANISATION) Training Supervision Budget Management Access to information				
OUCOMES (USER) Relationship of outcome to assessment Complains & problem solving Advocacy User – understanding participation satisfaction				

So how does the grid work? Remember it is a tool for visualizing how balanced an evaluation is likely to be before work on data collection and analysis actually begins. Like any good evaluation study, it starts with seeking clarity from the beginning. This is an eight stage process involved:

1 Identify exactly the service which is to be evaluated and why. This sounds simple, but it is worth the time to ensure that everyone involved is in transparent agreement about the extent and limits of the study's scope.

2 Brainstorm the questions to be answered by the evaluation. Do not try to prioritize these questions, just make sure that each question asks only one thing. They must not be "either/or" types of questions. Everyone involved should agree that the questions are relevant and useful.

3 Identify a data source for each question. Where and how are you going to get the data that answers the question?

4 Discard questions where no data source can be identified

5 Number the remaining questions (e.g. 1 – 20). This is not prioritizing, simply numbering the remaining questions in the order in which they were produced by the brainstorming.

6 Now turn to the grid and identify the box to which each question relates and enter the number of the question in the appropriate box. It is a matter for negotiation when a question seems to fit equally well into more than one box; in the end, each question number should be placed only in one box. Whichever box you agree on will be the right one. Every number must find a box.

7 Examine the grid. By looking at where the numbers appear on the grid you will be able to determine whether the evaluation is likely to be:

biased in any way – too many numbers in one box or in one column of boxes addressing one or two features only

service user focused – a spread of questions across the "outcomes (service user)" row of boxes and down the "interpersonal processes" and "continuity" columns of boxes would indicate a service user focus to the evaluation, addressing quality as well as quantity issues. A range of numbers across the outcome boxes may indicate that quality will be a significant characteristic of the evaluation result.

8 Amend and adjust the questions if necessary. If some boxes are too full of numbers whilst others remain empty, consider deleting some questions in the over-loaded boxes and replacing them with questions for the more empty boxes. This may seem difficult at first, so it may be useful to repeat steps 2-5, that is, brainstorm, identify data sources, discard questions which cannot be answered and number the questions. Then put that new number in the appropriate box. If there are empty boxes, consider whether you wish to evaluate that par-ticular feature of the work within the structure-process-outcome format. You may decide that further questions would not be useful.

Though evaluation is mentioned toward the end of this book, it must be a consideration at the very beginning of the service planning processes. Evaluation need not be a matter for only independent observers, with contrac-tual relationships with the agencies involved. This may be required from time to time for political reasons or for commissioning purposes. For the most part, however, practitioners themselves can evaluate their work regu-larly by learning to ask the right questions themselves. Evaluation becomes a powerful instrument of change when it combines the energies of practitioners and ser-vice users, working together to ensure that their services empower vulnerable people to improve the quality of their own lives.

Conclusion

THE pursuit of quality is a journey without end, but not without rewards. Most health care and social care professionals remain committed to helping other people maintain or improve the quality of life for themselves. Your commitment carries with it an obligation to probe the "mysteries" that surround your thinking about quality. Understanding the organisation within which you work can rescue your compassion for your service users and revive your sensitivity toward your colleagues. You must become or continue to be the empowered people who help others to empower themselves. Together you will gradually unfold a new perspective in health and social care, where services champion and foster only the well-being of the people for whom you design them. Organisational processes which fall short of this objective are unworthy and you may wish to leave them behind at some point along your way.

You and your organisation will be changing over the months and years ahead. Change is the only certainty! You may wish to return to this book from time to time, taking special care to look at your own notes in the margins. Use the book to take stock, to reflect, and to improve what you do for other people. It might help you to save your energies or to refocus them to achieve better outcomes for those who depend on you.

Glossary

ADVOCACY
Promoting or defending a cause by public or private debate or activity. Also, acting on behalf of another person or group of people to achieve that to which they believe themselves to be entitled.

ASSESSMENT
The recurring process of objectively identifying needs with and for the service users and their carers with a view to developing an individual service plan (see below) if necessary. An assessment helps clarify their needs in view of their living circumstances in order to come to an agreement about what should be done, if anything.

BENCH MARKING
A method of ensuring that all parts of the organisation operate as well as or better than any direct competitors by setting performance standards.

BOTTOM SLICING
The central reclaiming of funds after budgets have been devolved for specific services in order to fund other activities which will promote the effectiveness of those originally budgeted services.

CAPITAL
Finance required for non-recurring costs, such as building or equipment purchases.

CARE MANAGEMENT
The process of assessing need, purchasing services and coordinating those services to achieve agreed targeted outcomes for the service user.

CARE PACKAGE
A term commonly and sometimes unhelpfully used to describe a complexity of services designed to meet identified needs.

COMMISSIONING

The activity of identifying what needs exist, specifying services to meet those needs and contracting with agencies to ensure the services are provided. (Commissioning is not the same as purchasing: see below).

COMMUNITY CARE

The commissioning and provision of services to vulnerable people which enable them to maintain or increase their ability to remain living in the conditions and surroundings they choose.

COMMUNITY MENTAL HEALTH TEAM

A locality-based team offering specialist mental health services which benefit from the diversity of professional skills available within the multi-agency team itself.

COMPLAINT SYSTEM

A method of recording and responding to service user or carer concerns about quality. These systems present the opportunity to "recover" quality and promote customer loyalty and good will. Turn round times are important if people are to feel they are being taken seriously.

CONTRACT

A binding legal agreement which specifies the services to be provided, how and at what cost they will be provided, and to what standard they will be monitored.

DISCHARGE PLAN

A checklist of health and/or social care activities and services to be provided to a patient and their carers before or at the time of discharge from hospital.

DOMICILIARY CARE

Personal care arrangements which support the service user in a private residence.

DYNAMIC STANDARDS SETTING

A system of conceptualizing standards where structure and process are emphasized equally with outcome.

EMPOWERMENT

Doing whatever it takes to enable service users to do whatever it takes to achieve their own identified competencies and personal fulfilment and satisfaction.

EVALUATION
The process of assessing the value and effectiveness of services.

GP FUNDHOLDING
The process by which General Practitioners purchase primary or secondary health care services for patients from a practice held budget.

GAP ANALYSIS
Understanding the differences in expectations held by all the key stakeholders in any service. The analysis takes the form of a four stage interrogation:

— what is the gap between what the user expects and what the agency thinks the user expects?

— what is the gap between user/staff expectations and the service specification?

— what is the gap between specification and service delivered?

— what is the gap between service delivered and service publicized?

INDIVIDUAL SERVICE PLAN
A care plan developed after an assessment (see above) which specifies services to meet the individual health and social care needs identified by the assessment process. ISPs identify jointly agreed outcomes to be achieved by the services.

JOINT FINANCE
A system of financial management where health authorities allocate and administer funds to develop services which promote the effectiveness of health services.

KEY WORKER
The service provider professional who takes a co-ordinating role in the day to day activities specified by the care management role. The key worker is likely to have the most personal contact with the service users and carers.

MIXED ECONOMY
The use of independent service providers alongside publicly funded service providers across agency boundaries to achieve a common goal.

PRIMARY CARE
Health and social care provided in the community by professionals working by themselves or together with professionals from other disciplines or agencies.

PROVIDER
A person or agency who or which supplies health or social care services in accordance with a contract (above) or service level agreement (below).

PURCHASING
Buying health and social care services from an identified budget and in accord with a contract or service level agreement established by the commissioning process (see above).

QUALITY CIRCLES
Small groups of individuals resolving problems which effect all processes or outcomes for which they share responsibility.

REVENUE
Finance required for recurring costs, such as staffing, service provision and running expenses.

RING FENCING
Isolation of a sum of money or other resources for a specific purpose.

SECONDARY CARE
Health or social care provided in a facility with specialized services and centralized expertise.

SERVICE LEVEL AGREEMENT
A non-legally binding but written arrangement within an organisation or between the organisation and an individual employee or group of employees which specifies services to be provided, how they will be provided and at what cost, and to what standard they will be monitored. A service level agreement is not a contract (see above).

SERVICE SPECIFICATIONS
The minimum service or process requirements of a contracted or agreed service.

SLIPPAGE
The description of the effect on a capital budget or joint
finance when funds remain unspent within the planned
timescale.

TERTIARY CARE
Highly specialized health or social care services available
to a few service users within a wide population catchment
area. A period of residence in the specialized facility is usually associated with this level of care.

TOP SLICING
The central retention of funds before budgets are devolved
for specific service activities in order to fund other activities
of overall agency interest .

Appendix 1

VISION	what the future should look like
PURPOSE	the destination, what is going to be achieved in making that future
VALUES	the landscape, the perspective that is believed to be most effective to realise PURPOSE
VISION + PURPOSE + VALUES POLICY	Statement of operational values to be employed and objectives to be achieved in realising PURPOSE
STRATEGY	the map and the itinerary, a statement of the rules of engagement of POLICY values and objectives, giving direction and timescales
PLANNING	sorting out the backpack, the preparatory thinking required, the application of strategy to practical realities, the decision making that leads to goal-setting and change, something different happening, something better happening
IMPLEMENTATION	stepping out making something better happen
STANDARDS	the road signs gauging progress toward short or medium term goals as the means of achieving the PURPOSE
STRUCTURE	the road networks the organisational framework to sustain PURPOSEful activity
TACTICS	the shortcuts to energy efficiency in achieving POLICY values and objectives

EVALUATION	seeing how far you have come/how far you have yet to go, the review of outcomes against policy and strategy, the decision making that leads to REVISION
REVISION	getting it right again for the new future

Bibliography

Aarons, Maureen., Gittens, Tessa., The Handbook of Autism, A guide for Parents and Professionals, 1993

Argyris, C., and Schonn, D., Organisational Learning, Addison Wesley, 1978.

Berne, E., Games People Play

Bowling Ann. Measuring Health 1993

Calero, H., and Oskam, B., Negotiate For What Your Want, Thorsons, 1982.

Covey, Stephen R. The 7 Habits of Highly Effective People, Powerful lessons in Personal Challenge, 1989.

Crosby, P.B., Quality is Free, McGraw-Hill.

De Bono Edward.

    Atlas of Management Thinking

    Conflicts

    Lateral Thinking. 1970

    Practical Thinking. 1971

    Tactics

    Thinking Course

Donabedian, Avedis. The Definition of Quality and Approaches to its Assessment, 1980

Handy Charles B. Understanding Organisations. 1985

Peters, T.J., and Waterman, R.H., In Search of Excellence: Lessons from America's Best-Run Companies. Harper+Row, 1984.

Rhodes Jerry. Conceptual Toolmaking, Expert systems of the mind.

Blackwell 1991.

Ryecroft, C., Anxiety and Neurosis, Pelican, 1970.

Shea, M., Influence.

Index

This is not an exhaustive index. It is intended to help locate key topics and other points of interest in the text. It does not include terms occurring very frequently throughout the book, such as "service user". Main subject headings can be found by consulting the contents pages.

index

P

protocols, 63
providers/providing, 39, 41, 47, 73, 81, 82, 88, (defined) 98
public health report, 9
public meetings, 39
purchasers/purchasing, 6, 9, 40, 47, 95, 96, (defined) 98
purpose (main entry only), 11-16

Q

qualitative data, 55, 76
quality circles, 98
quality of life, 1, 13, 26, 57, 81, 93
quantitative techniques, 76
questioning, 1, 11
questionnaires, 9

R

reconfiguration, 22
red herrings, 48
re-engineering, 22
records, 55, 76, 80, (user held) 32, 39
rent, 78
research, 53, 83-85
resistance, 21, 47-50, 65, 71
restructuring, 16, 22, 54
revenue, (defined) 98
ring fencing, (defined) 98
rowing crew, 51
rules of engagement, 58

S

secondary care, (defined) 98
self-esteem, 70, 74, 77
self-management, 31, 36, 37, 40

service level agreement, (defined) 98
service specifications, (defined) 99
service user representatives, 57
siege mentality, 49
skill deficits, 70, 80
slippage (defined), 99
social clubs, 78
social outcomes, 75, 81-82
spreadsheet, 78-81
staff shortages, 70, 80
standards, 6, 13, 16, 19-21, 25, 28, 82, 95, 96
strategy, 13, 58, 59-60, 63, (defined) 101
structures, 13, 15-16, 22, 24, 86
sustaining organisation, 24
SWOT, 67, 68
systems culture, 24

T

team culture test, 54
team managers, 45
team skill toolbox, 52
tertiary care, (defined) 99
timescale/timetable, 13, 59, 85, 101
top slicing, (defined) 99
top-down planning, 61
training, 17, 40, 52, 63, 67, 70, 88
trusts, 57, 81

U

useless values, 18
user groups, 39
user/client held records, 32, 39

V

value for money, 7

V

values, 13, 15, 16-19, 20, 22, 28,
   58, 59, 60, 62, 72, 76, 101
vision, 6, 13, 14, 15, 25, 41, 57-62,
   72, 88
voluntary agencies, 57
vulnerable people, 2, 26, 44, 91

W

withholding information, 32